EVERYTHING YOU ALWAYS WANTED TO KNOW ABOUT HOME VIDEO EDITING

(But Nobody Had the Answers)

A one-on-one, very easy-to-understand consumer guide on what to buy, what accessories to use, how to film and how to edit your videos.

From the author of "EVERYTHING YOU
ALWAYS WANTED TO KNOW ABOUT VIDEO
(But Nobody Had the Answers)"
And
"EVERYTHING YOU
ALWAYS WANTED TO KNOW ABOUT CAMCORDERS
(But Nobody Had the Answers)"

John P. Johnston

COVER PHOTOGRAPH:

C.A. BARBIER
805 Norte Dame
Lachine, Que'
H8S2B8

Approved by: Professional
Videographers
Association of
America

COVER DESIGN & LAYOUT: John P. Johnston &
William Carter

Printed by Griffin Printing

ISBN 1-877725-15-3

SGH Publications, Inc
2320 St. Louis
St. Lazare, Québec
J0P1V0

(514) 426-8130

Table of Contents

In the Field Production Checklist

Camcorder______________________________
Back-up Camcorder______________________
Extra Batteries________1 ________2 ____________
(Make sure that they are fully charged from the last job) _____
AC Battery Charger ______________________
DC Car Battery Charger ___________________
Blank Video Tapes _____1 ________2 ________3 ________
Tripod________________________________
Geneva Video Head Cleaner ________________
Shoulder Brace or Steadycam_______________
Video Light ____________________________
Extra Batteries________1 ________2 ____________
Extra Double ACA Lines 1 ________2 ____________
Extra Microphones_______________________
____________________CAM-EAR____________
____________________Wireless ____________
____________________Wired ______________
Back-up Batteries for Microphones __________
Portable CG (Character Generator)__________
Portable Color Monitor (Or B&W) ___________
Extra VCR(s) Depending on the job _1 ________2 ________
SEG (Special Effects Generator) Depending on the job ______

SPECIAL EQUIPMENT FOR THIS PRODUCTION: ________
1______________________________________
2______________________________________
3______________________________________
4______________________________________

The author and the Publisher of this book have agreed that because of it's importance, you have permission to reprint this page ONLY.

WHO MAKES WHAT?

When buying a Camcorder you may notice that one looks very much like another; a Panasonic looks like a Quasar for instance. That's because they are both made by Matsushita. Below is a chart of Who's Who, or What's What in Camcorders.

VHS/Super-VHS

Company	**What brands they make.**
Goldstar	Goldstar
Hitachi	Hitachi, RCA, Sears, Minolta, Realistic, Pentax
JVC	JVC, Zenith
Matsushita	Chinon, GE, Olympus, Sylvania, Curtis Mathis, Instant Replay, Panasonic, Quasar, Phillips, Magnavox, Teknika

8mm/Hi-8

Company	What brands they make
Canon	Canon, Sunpak
Hitachi	Minolta, Pentax
Matsushita	Nikon, Olympus
Sanyo	Sanyo, Fisher
Sony	Sony, Kyocera, Nikon, Ricoh

INTRODUCTION

Greetings! It is my intention in this book to give you a no-nonsense, extremely valuable guide to all phases of consumer video editing; from what equipment is needed to the finishing touches.

We have made this book easy to understand for everybody, not just the rocket scientists among us. The owner's manuals that come with your Camcorders and other video equipment do not tell you the fundamentals of video production, like the in and out principal of video equipment.

We have spiced up this book a little with SmileyCam™ to help focus on important parts of production and protecting your equipment to make it last longer.

In this guide I will try to stay away from using specific brand names or model numbers, mainly because VCRs and Camcorders may change model numbers two or three times a year and we want our books to be able to be used with all video equipment from 1975 for years to come. I have however, named some brands that are not apt to change model numbers, and I would fully endorse and have permitted advertising of these superior products in this book.

Since this book is written for the video novice to the professional videographer, I will take you from simple equipment buying to advanced hookup. From the simple SEG (Special Effects Generator) to the studio broadcast quality equipment. I've added my personal views as a video expert and even some humor. It is my hope that this book will be of help to video enthusiasts and novices alike.

BUYING EQUIPMENT

WHAT IS A CAMCORDER?

Unlike the separate video camera hooked by an umbilical cord to a video recorder unit of just a few years ago, a Camcorder (Video Camera and Video Recorder in one portable unit) has become the wave of the future.

There are four formats of Camcorders: VHS, VHS-C, BETA (which is no longer being produced) and 8mm. These four formats are subdivided down even further into: VHS, S-VHS, DIGITAL VHS, S-VHS DIGITAL, VHS-C, S-VHS-C, DIGITAL S-VHS-C, BETA, SUPER BETA, ED BETA, 8MM, DIGITAL 8MM, and HI-8MM. They range in weight from 2.2 lbs to upwards of 12 lbs (loaded).

The new Camcorders function like the older two-piece units except they do not have the tuner/timer function that you would find on your home deck VCR. It's that simple. Also the Camcorders of today have a lot more automatic features than the two-piece units.

BUYING A CAMCORDER (The Heart of Your Editing System)

With the advent of flying erase-heads, video/audio insert editing and digital effects, the Camcorder is fast becoming a portable production studio boasting over 400 horizontal lines of resolution in S-VHS, or HI-8MM; flying erase heads (for clean cuts) in all 8mm and most hi-end VHS; a wide variety of digital effects (wipes from one scene to another, stroboscopic effects, mosaic and painting effects, to digital 30 plus power zoom); and video/audio insert editing (available in few 8mm, and the majority of $1,200 or more full-sized VHS Camcorders).

When you buy your Camcorder, keep in mind that it is the heart of your productions. The more that you are able to do with your Camcorder in the field, the less you will have to edit and worry about later. There have been many weddings where I striped a tape, added titles, transferred photos onto a video tape before the wedding, did good filming the day of the wedding, did the audio dub in my van, and had a great finished product half an hour after the reception. I did not have to go back to the studio and spend hours editing because with the help of the flying erase head (for clean cuts and video inserts) and the audio dubbing capability (adding music without affecting the video portion of the tape), I was able to finish the job in the field.

To make a long story short, get the most features you can afford in the Camcorder you buy.

If you have purchased a Camcorder without a flying erase head and video/audio insert editing, every time you turn the Camcorder on and off you will notice a very distracting color bar squiggle down the picture. This is called a moiré line. This is eliminated with a flying erase head. If you want to add music, or if you want to insert new video over old video (between scenes) on the master tape, you have to have video/audio insert capabilities. You can get these capabilities on a deck unit VCR but at a cost of $700 on up. So it would benefit you to consider spending a couple of hundred dollars and getting a second Camcorder. This is like having your cake and eating it too, since a deck unit VCR cannot act as a camera, but a Camcorder can act as a deck unit VCR. In my productions, I always take a second Camcorder with me in case the main Camcorder goes down.

S-VHS is great, but if you are filming a house for insurance purposes or filming any job where you have to immediately turn over the production, do not use the S-VHS mode of your Camcorder. It cannot play in a conventional VHS machine. (It will look as if it was filmed on another planet.) 8mm or Hi-8mm does a wonderful job but here again, it has to be transferred to standard VHS before it can be of use to the general consumer.

Below is an illustration of some of the neat Digital Effects in a digital Camcorder.

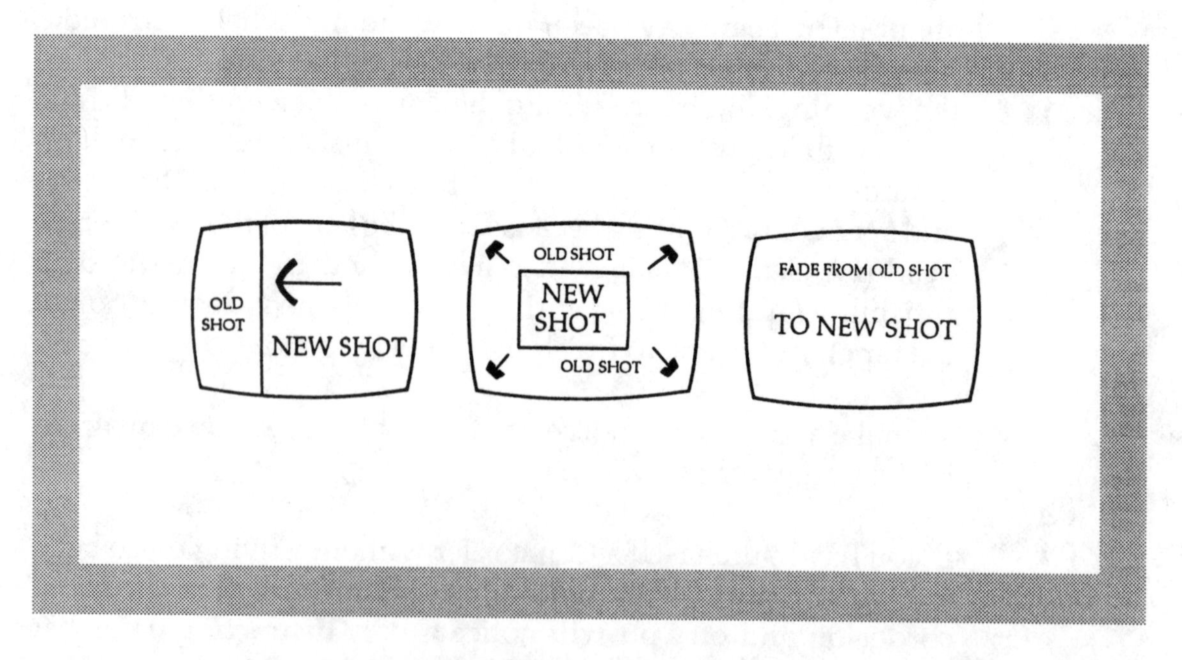

Along with these effects, you can also get things like mosaic (turns the picture into tiny blocks or pixels); digital still (this allows you to still a shot, much like a picture for as long as you want to film it); stroboscopic effect (looks like your subject is under a strobe light); and digital fading (allows you to fade from a digital still picture to a new live picture). There are a host of other special effects like the mirrored effect (featured on America's Home Videos) which allows the screen to be split down the middle, and the left half mirrored to the right half. It sounds weird but the man who submitted it won $10,000 that week. Not bad for a Camcorder that only cost $1,595 retail.

The last two things on digital that I would like to mention are the 30 to 1 digital zoom, which will increase the zoom from a 10 or 12 to 1 zoom, to 30 to 1 or more, using digital technology (the quality will suffer slightly); and EIS system (Electronic Image Stabilization). This is where the image is digitally suspended, (much like floating in water), so that when small jerks occur the image stays stable. These small jerks will normally occur while doing something like panning, walking, (you should never try to walk with a Camcorder), or filming from a boat. With this effect there is a slight loss in picture quality also.

My best advice before you buy a Camcorder is to ask yourself what you are going to do with it over the next two years. If you are going to transfer photos, movie film, slides or do a project like a wedding, buy the most you can afford. Remember however to add from $300 to $500 to your Camcorder purchase for things like a tripod, extra batteries, microphones, hard or soft carrying case and, yes, even repair insurance.

SmileyCam™

VIDEO INSURANCE
(The Murphy's Law Effect)

No matter how much you spend on a Camcorder, if something goes wrong, it will cost you big bucks to repair it after the standard 90-day parts and labor or 1 year parts warranty wears out. If you do end up having to take your Camcorder to a repair service, it will cost you an average of $125.00 just to have him look at it and then an average repair cost of between $85 and $240.

A five-year extended warranty for parts and labor runs from $139 to $185. Before you get an extended warranty, find out if it will cover your equipment if you move to another state. Also, check into the company that the store recommends to you. (The salesman does get a kick back for the insurance he sells, so don't take his word alone about the policy.) I once bought a Camcorder at one store and went to another store and got the extended warranty for less money. So do some shopping before you put your money down.

I would not recommend an extended warranty on a VCR that cost less than $450. I would recommend it for anything over that plus 28" TVs or Monitor/Receivers, (it is an absolute must for any Camcorder). Make sure that if you buy a Camcorder under a business name that it will be covered. Some extended warranty insurance companies will not cover it if it is under your business name. If you want us to recommend an extended warranty company, please contact us by letter or phone (from the information in the back of this book), and we would be happy to refer you to a nation-wide company (no kick backs involved).

TRADEMARK FRAUD (Captain VHS™)

Now that I have your attention from reading the title of this section, let me explain.

You may own non-registered video tapes. The tapes that are properly registered will have the following symbol VHS somewhere on the case (this **exact** symbol, not just a close approximation). Some people will try to fool you by putting something that resembles this logo on their non-registered tapes. Having this logo (like Captain VHS™) does not mean the tape is the best, but it does mean that it meets certain specifications as to case design, video tape construction, etc. Do not buy any video tape that does not have this exact VHS mark. These companies are real tricksters. The VHS logo looks similar to Captain VHS™, but not quite.

Some of the prerecorded movies are put on non-registered video tapes. An example of this would be some of the children's tapes that you see for under $15.

In a Camcorder use the best video tape that you can afford.

VIDEO ACCESSORIES
(The Walk Before You Fly Section)

It is essential that, before you film anything or do video editing, you need to equip yourself to do a proper job, and also protect your equipment. Here are some products that are a "must have" for any videographer.

THE "MUST HAVE" ACCESSORY

Haze Filter: Do not use your Camcorder without one. This is the same kind of thing that you may have bought for your 35mm camera. It screws on the front of your lens to protect it (from rocks, kids, dirt that will scratch your lens, etc.). If your video store does not have one to fit your Camcorder, a camera store will. They cost between $10 - $12 and they are the cheapest insurance in the world to protect your investment. No professional photographer is ever without one, and no professional videographer should go without one either.

The EyeOpener™

The EyeOpener™ is also a "must-have" accessory. It is a small device that hooks to the eyepiece of your video camera or Camcorder that will enable you to avoid squinting, and it lets you use both eyes. Without the EyeOpener™, if you are looking through the eyepiece with your right eye you have to squint. If you don't, you can't see the EVF (Electronic View Finder) and thus what you are filming.

The EyeOpener™ will give you back your peripheral vision so you can see a kamikaze kid heading for your tripod as well as making your eyepiece picture look twice as big.

If you are still not convinced, try this. Film a wedding and reception for three hours or walk around the house for an hour or so with your left eye closed. Had enough? So ....? Go pick one up. It only takes a minute to install (it folds away after use).

The Eyeopener™ Eliminates Binocular Rivalry

So You Don't Have To Close One Eye To Film

ATTACHING THE EYEOPENER TO THE CAMERA

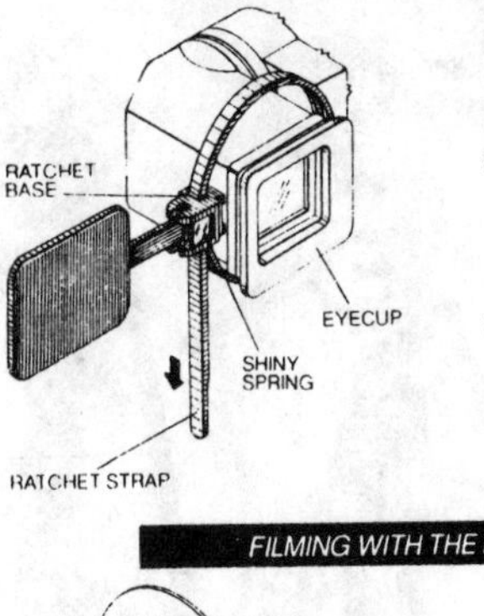

1. *Position the Eyeopener™ on the camera viewfinder as illustrated. The shiny spring must face the rear of the camera as shown.*
2. *Slide the Eyeopener™ close to the end of the viewfinder. Slip the ratchet strap through the ratchet base and tighten very tight!*
3. *After tightening the strap as tight as possible, clip off all the excess strap with a fingernail clipper.*

RATCHET BASE
EYECUP
SHINY SPRING
RATCHET STRAP

FILMING WITH THE EYEOPENER

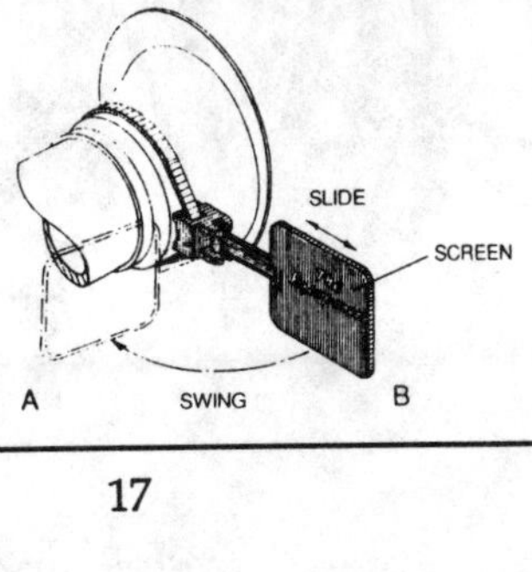

To use, swing the screen to position B (position A is for storage). Slide the screen side to side to maximize peripheral vision while maintaining a clear image through the camera.

SLIDE
SCREEN
A
SWING
B

VIDEO TRIPODS

Tripods are not created equal. Video tripods are different than camera tripods in several ways. Video tripods are taller than camera tripods (or should be). They should have a fluid head for smoother operation. You don't have to pan with a photo camera as you do with video. Try to get one with a quick release (this saves a lot of time). It should have a middle support brace. Always use a heavy-duty video tripod for VHS or S-VHS Camcorders. Take your video camera with you to the store to try it out. It will cost you about $99 to $150 for VHS-C or 8mm and $150 or more for VHS or S-VHS. No joke. There is a 99% chance that, if the tripod falls over and the Camcorder hits the ground, it is going to go to the video hospital. This is one thing you don't want to be cheap about.

EXTRA LENSES

On occasion you may need a special lens. I break down lenses into two groups: Extension lenses and Special Effects lenses. Before you run out and buy any extra lenses, there are a few things you should know:

1. Video lenses are not cheap. Lenses can be as inexpensive as $49 or as expensive as $150 to $600

2. With most telephoto lenses or wide angle lenses you have to use them on manual zoom and focus settings on your Camcorder.

3. Try to wait until you have a video job that requires a special lens and then include at least 1/2 the cost of the lens into the production cost of that job.

4. Always take your Camcorder into the store and try the lenses on it before you buy. You may need size adapters to fit the lens onto your Camcorder.

Now, let's talk about the different types and kinds of lenses.

Extension Lenses

Telephoto lens: A telephoto lens is great at filming shots that are off into the distance, and you cannot get close enough with your normal zoom capabilities or your Camcorder. Precautions should be taken, however. When using any telephoto lens, make sure the Camcorder is on a tripod. Never walk with a Camcorder but rather use the leap frog effect. Zoom out, stop the Camcorder, walk about 30-50 feet and zoom out again. Also, remember, with a telephoto lens attached you probably will have to use your unit on manual focus and manual zoom.

Wide Angle Lens: A wide angle lens is mostly used in close quarters, such as a living room around Christmas. This lens is also used in the manual mode, but focusing is done in the macro mode of your Camcorder.

Hemispheric lens: This is a next-generation, wide-angle lens which offers a very wide, distorted view, creating a fish bowl effect. This view covers almost 180 degrees. This is good for great creative videography.

SPECIAL EFFECTS LENSES

You can do a lot with special effects lenses. You can change the mood of your production, add emphasis to certain parts of your filming and last, but not least, you can do more before going to your editing deck, so it should save you time and headaches later.

Multi-image Lens: This lens usually will allow you to have a constant steady picture in the middle and up to nine duplicates circling around the middle image. Kind of like the attack of the fly effect. I used a multi-image lens at Disneyland and zoomed in on Mickey's tail, then added mosquito sound effects. OK, so I have a warped sense of humor.

Star-Point Lens: These are called by several names, but their function is the same. When attached to a Camcorder and pointed at any light source, they will highlight the source into a star or cross effect. This is great with Las Vegas-style lighting or highlighting a shiny dress or jewelry.

Colored Filters: These are great for situations with too much light. A polarized lens will help. A rose or red for sunsets, or a brown for Sepia or old-time effect (this looks great in a small section of a wedding). Colored filters can also be used if you don't have the bucks for an SEG (Special Effects Generator).

Portrait Lens: You can buy these or make your own. This effect is one of the center being in focus while the outside border is out of focus. I call this a portrait effect after studio-type photography where the subject looks like there is an aura around them. One of the oldest tricks in photography is putting Vaseline on a clear filter or a UV haze filter to create that same effect. So save some bucks and break out the grease.

Cut-Outs: You can go wild with cut-outs. Binoculars, clipboards, hearts, diamonds, your creative mind is your only limit. Just take a piece of cardboard and use an X-acto knife to cut out the shape, spray paint it black and then hold it up in front of the camera while shooting. You may have to put your Camcorder into the manual focus mode depending on how much of the edges are being used.

I hope this section has given you some ideas. I hope you will use some of them and I'm sure you have some ideas of your own. Remember: no matter how weird it is, if it looks good, film it!

CARRYING CASES (The Hard and the Soft of the Matter)

People have always asked me, once they have purchased a video camera or Camcorder, do they need a case? If so, is it better to have a hard or a soft case?

The answer to the first question is a big YES. The question of which type is a little more difficult. If you take a lot of trips (airplanes, boats, buses, etc.) get a hard case. It will protect your equipment better. But, if you putter around the house or take short day trips, you might want to consider a soft case (what I call a day bag). Now, the bag does not have to hold everything you own for the Camcorder (the hard case should). It needs to be able to carry the Camcorder, batteries and, most important, the battery charger. I don't know how many times tourists have come into my stores and asked me to charge their batteries because they left the battery charger at home. Make sure that the soft case is padded, especially on the bottom and outfacing side. Also, make sure it has the ability to carry an extra blank tape (just in case).

I have seen a lot of Camcorder bags. I like the features of the Movitec bags because of the extra padding in the shoulder strap, the detachable inner accessory pouch, the **angled** strap to stay on your shoulder and the vinyl clothes guard on the back of the bag.

EXTRA PROTECTION (Can't Get Enough of a Good Thing)

OK, so you've trekked across the country that made National Lampoon's Vacation look like a girl scout trip. You've made it to Disneyland and all the best attractions. Do you really want to carry a hard or soft case all day long? Arnold Schwartzenegger would not do that. Well then, how are you going to protect your Camcorder from the mobs of bodies with but one thought on their minds—crush the guy with the Camcorder! You see, a Camcorder looks something like a football, and you are the quarterback at a Superbowl game. Now, instead of using your wife or kids to block for you, a company out of Washington came up with a great idea. It's called a ProPak-1 and it protects the Camcorder when it's being used. This is when most of your damage occurs. It's ready in about three seconds (we timed it). It's also great at the beach. We actually buried a Camcorder in the ProPak-1 and not a bit of sand got through.

Made by CAM GLOVE INC, they are available in VHS models only.

EXTRA BATTERY PACKS (Are They Needed?)

That, of course, depends on your use. If you just bought your Camcorder, don't buy any extra battery packs until you find out if you really need them. You might be able to use a car-cord adapter that would let you charge your battery from your car cigarette lighter (I've only seen these for 8mm, but they may sell them for VHS also). When I used mine at Disneyland, I filmed till lunch, recharged my battery during lunch, and then finished the day with just the one battery. Neat, huh?

Note: The batteries in a Camcorder are usually NI-CAD type which means that you have to charge them and discharge them a few times to bring them up to full capacity. The other alternative would be a battery belt or pack, with a car-cord adapter. These offer several times the capability of the standard battery and (a good point here), if you sell your equipment, you can use the battery pack or belt for portable radios, TVs, CDs or any new video equipment or Camcorders. So, think before you buy.

LED ENERGY CHECKER

You can now buy batteries that let you check visually to see if the battery is charged or if it needs to be charged. To me, it's one of the greatest inventions since sliced bread. I get tired of charging all of my batteries, if I don't use them for a month or so, when all I really have to do is push a button to see if I have enough charge to do a film shoot. This feature will also increase the life of your batteries because you would not have to charge them up as frequently.

TURBO CAMCHARGER

The main problem with Camcorder batteries is "Memory". If you have a two-hour battery but only use it for 1/2 hour or one hour over and over again, the battery will develop a memory. Then, when you need it for a two-hour job it will only play for an hour.

To overcome this memory effect and be able to charge your battery from your car, you need a Turbo Camcharger from Arkon Resources.

Sure, you could buy a unit for $49 - 69 just to get rid of the memory effect, but you still would have to spend about $95 to be able to charge your battery from your car. Then you would have to spend between $29 - $49 for a car-cord adapter. Why not get it all in one unit? You save some money and don't have to carry tons of stuff around. I have spent a lot of time and money finding these products that will help you do the best job with the least amount of money.

**TURBO CAMCHARGER™
OUT PERFORMS YOUR
ORIGINAL EQUIPMENT
BATTERY CHARGER**

DC Capability ...

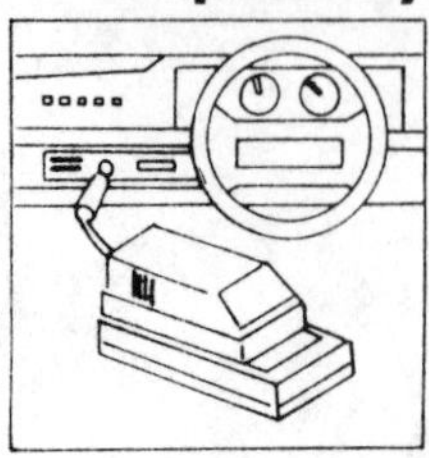

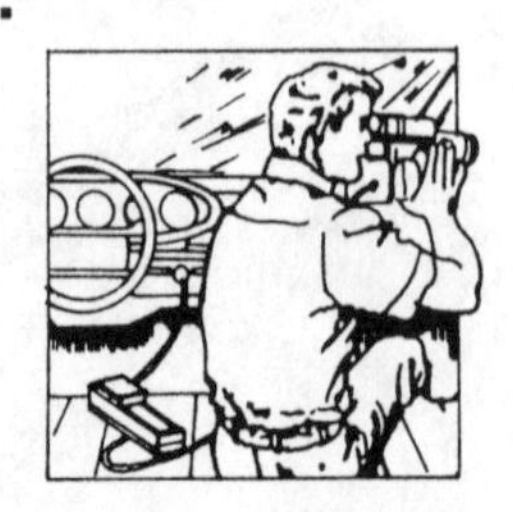

AC Capability ...

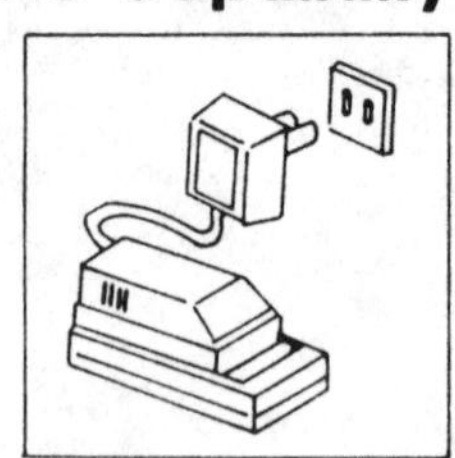

You can contact Arkon Resources, Inc. about the Turbo Camcharger at (818) 358-1133.

EXTERNAL MICROPHONES
(Say it Again, Sam)

Of all the Camcorders with built-in microphones, the 8mm records the best sound (without motor noise from the Camcorder). Unlike the older two-piece units of days past, the Camcorder (or more specifically the VHS, S-VHS, and even the Digital S-VHS Camcorders) record a faint motor noise, especially when recording in a quiet room. This weird hum drives you crazy if you are going to film interviews, for example. You almost have to have an external microphone (most Camcorders have a jack for an external microphone). You can even buy wireless remote microphones now.

Let's talk about wireless remote microphones. This is one of the products that you should definitely check out at the store, or try at home, before going out to do a wedding. Because it is wireless, you may pick up interference from such things as CB radios. This is definitely one of those products where you get what you pay for.

Let's get into wired microphones. You may or may not need a powered microphone (depending on your Camcorder). You need to take it to a store and try it out. The ones that you buy as an accessory from the manufacturer are usually expensive.

CAM EAR™

A CAM EAR™ is a Camcorder mounted Audio Zoom Microphone. We have tested a lot of units (mainly because we own VHS Camcorders), and found the CAM EAR™ to be the best for several reasons:

1. *Audio Zoom control*
2. *Directional pick-up*
3. *Retail $89.95*
4. *100% made in the USA*
5. *Uses it's own battery*
6. *Mounts on any Camcorder*
7. *Lightweight (5.4 ounces)*
8. *On/Off indicator light (other wired microphones don't have this)*
9. *Reduces background, camera, and wind noises*
10. *Looks neat (kind of Hi-tech)*

The key to CAM EAR's™ performance is the Audio Zoom control, which can be set at any point from "near", when you are within 10 feet of your subject, to "Far", to record subjects at a distance up to 50 feet. Great to cover weddings and outside interviews without getting the high-pitched sound of kids on tape.

CAM EAR FEATURES –

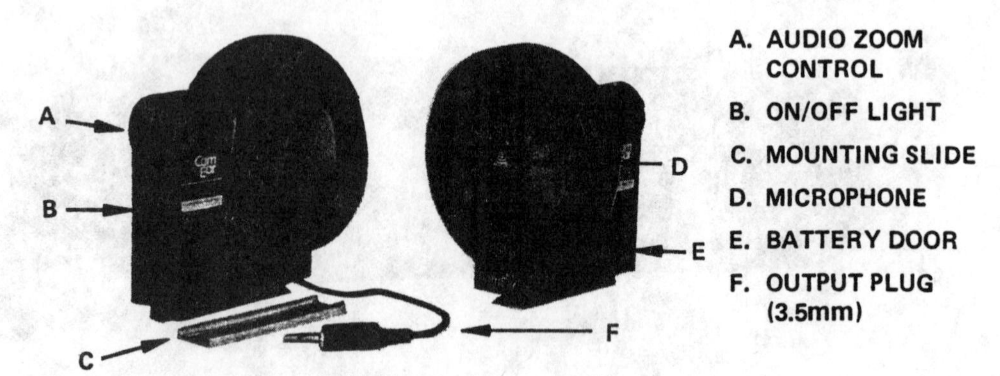

CAM EAR™ can be used with any Camcorder that has an "external microphone" jack (most Camcorders have this feature). It can be mounted on any Camcorder, either in the Camcorder's shoe attachment, or by using CAM EAR's™ self-adhesive mounting shoe.

CAM EAR™ is powered by it's own 9-volt battery (easy to find), so it will not reduce the life of your Camcorder battery. I love the On/Off indicator light. Most wired microphones don't have this feature, so you don't know if it's going to work or not.

Contact TC Electronics (Canada) Ltd. at (514) 426-3010 for more info and how to get your CAM EAR™ now!

VIDEO LIGHTING

There are two types of video lighting: AC and DC. AC usually ranges from 150 to 600 watts or more. These are primarily used in a studio situation. DC usually ranges from 25 to 150 watts. The thing to remember here is that video lights EAT POWER. I had a 150-watt light that ate up a six-hour battery belt in 50 minutes.

I suggest that you stick with lights in the 35 to 100-watt range. Also make sure that your light has a guard over the bulb. There are two reasons for this:

1) To prevent damage to the light.

2) If you touch the light bulb with your bare hands the oil from your fingers will cause the bulb to either burn out immediately or within a matter of minutes. Replacement bulbs are NOT cheap.

Since everyone's situation is different it is hard for me to recommend one particular light that will fit every need. All I can say is research before you buy.

WARNING: Anything worth saying is worth repeating. DO NOT touch a video lightbulb with your bare hands whether it is ON or OFF.

LUX: THE TRUE STORY
(One Candle Too Low)

It seems that one of the only things people know when looking for a Camcorder nowadays is to look for the LUX rating and get the lowest LUX. The misconception they have is that they think that with a seven LUX camera they can record a candle on a cake. At least it looks that way on TV. If you try this it will turn out very colorless, dark and grainy looking. As an example, let's go down to one LUX. First, no one will confirm this one LUX rating. Even most of the owner's manuals say "approaching 1 LUX". In the owner's manuals it even suggests that optimum light intensity on the optical image is 1500 LUX which is 150 footcandles. This rating was taken directly from an owner's manual of a Digital S-VHS current model Camcorder (Top Line).

I am not trying to project an air of gloom. I am just pointing out that we still cannot record properly in very low light conditions. If you plan on buying a Camcorder for a lot of low light conditions, plan also on buying video lights to go with it.

There is no standard test by which consumer Camcorders are judged, you are literally at the mercy of the manufacturer. To prove the point once and for all, here is how the equipment is tested.

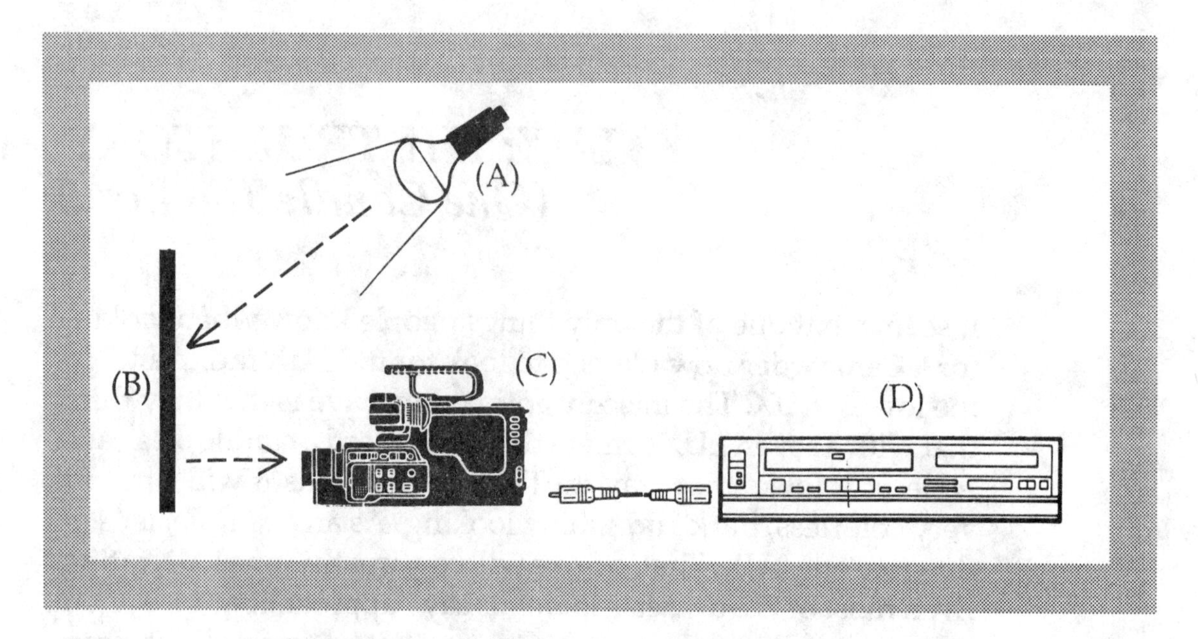

Light source (A) illuminates back drop (B) the reflected light is picked up by Camcorder (C) and is then transferred to test equipment (D).

Now, if different testing companies use a bulb of different brightness (75 watt/100 watt) or the distance between (A) and (B), or (B) and (C) is different, you will get a different reading in (D).

In plain English folks, LUX, since there is no standard test, does not exist. Four different companies could test the equipment and they would get four different readings. So, if a salesman is telling you that there is a uniform, fair system of testing, you tell him for me that he doesn't know what he's talking about. Even though a Camcorder nowadays had a 3 to 10 LUX rating (1 LUX = 1 lm/m2), video cameras and Camcorders require more than 100 LUX to produce a sharp, high-contrast, low-noise picture, with good color.

So try out a Camcorder for it's real light capabilities before you buy.

VIDEO FILMING

HOW TO MAKE MONEY IN VIDEO (Long Green Section)

With the quality of video cameras today, you can make a large amount of money with a Camcorder. I started my videotaping business with just $300. I placed some ads in the local newspaper saying that I did film-to-video transfers, transferred photos and slides onto video tape, and filmed houses for insurance purposes.

My first job was a wedding. I rented a video camera outfit from the local cable company for $45. I charged $350 to do the wedding, made two copies (one for $20 with a case and one for $15 without a case), and spent $3 for gas. Tapes and cases cost me $20 and I walked out with $282 clear in my pocket. Not too bad for a day's work.

The next job I got was to transfer slides onto video for $640. I bought a new slide projector for $210, a special adapter for a video camera for $120, went to a store and put a video camera on my credit card (payments $32 per month), spent $20 for background music, spent $10 for tapes and cases. I set aside $96 for three monthly payments on the new video equipment, worked a day and a half on the job, and walked out with $194, a slide projector (forever), slide adapter (forever), and payments on the video camera.

Within four months I opened my first store, and within two years my business was worth over $750,000. Of course, all of that was not just video production since we also sold video equipment.

It was not quite as easy as I have made it appear. At the time I was doing this, I also worked full time with the local cable company. *All* the money from the video production went back into buying more equipment and advertising, etc. But, there is no reason why every one of you can't make money in video, whether you want to make a full-time business out of it or just pay for your video equipment. The money is there if you know how to do it. I am going to unlock the secrets to home video production (the right way), so that you can give a quality product at a fair price. Please, for your credibility (and for my peace of mind), follow these guides to the letter. Do not cut corners. Give a quality product.

HOW TO STRIPE A VIDEO TAPE
(The Dawn of a New Beginning)

What's good for Paramount, Tri-Star, MGM, and Universal is good enough for you. A beginning stripe has several purposes: it gets your name out there; it shows the copyright of your production; it gives your copying warning (good luck); and it looks good and professional.

To stripe a tape takes time, but you only have to do this once a year or two. (All you do for the second and third years is change the date, so make at least two tapes, maybe three.) You may want to change them after two years.

You start by taking a short, blank tape (use a 10 minute tape if you can), and insert it into your Camcorder or portable video deck unit. Leaving your lens cap on, record about 20 seconds on the front of the video tape (if you can disconnect or unplug your microphone, do so). This method is used to eliminate the drop out left over from previous recordings at the beginning of the tape as on rental movies. You also could hook up to an SEG and put up a black field.

Next, put up the titles on the screen as illustrated below:

Production of
Video One Publications

Copyright 1991

All rights reserved

You can follow this with:

WARNING

Any commercial use or duplication of this copyright material without prior written permission is forbidden by Federal law. Violators may be subject to civil and/or criminal penalties.

(Title 17, United States Code, Sections 501 and 506)

You may want to follow this with:

For information or copies contact:

Video One Publications
3474 Dromedary Way Ste. 1304
Las Vegas, NV 89115

When this is done you can fade out to black again for about one minute. Depending on your CG (Character Generator) and/or your Gen-Lock capabilities (which gives you the ability to add titles over the top of the video), you can put any type of background behind your titles, such as the front of your store, or you filming, or the world turning.

Add some background music, and there you go. You have your Master Stripe Tape. Now, every time you do a production, just copy your master stripe tape onto your production tape. It looks great, professional, and will get you more business with a short plug for your company.

You can do this even if it's for family and friends. For example:

Production of:

The
Smith
Family

Copyright: There's a date somewhere on the film.

Followed by:

WARNING

This video was done for the fun of it.

You touch, I break!

This is just an idea, but it will look better than nothing at all.

Caution: if you do not stripe a tape, please still put the cover over the lens and run the Camcorder for about 20-30 seconds on a new tape. This is because most dropouts on the tape happen in the beginning.

TRANSFERRING PHOTOGRAPHS ONTO VIDEO TAPE

Equipment Needed

1) A camcorder or two-piece video camera and recorder with video and audio insert editing, plus a macro setting. Preferably with a flying erase head.

2) A good tripod.

3) A stereo.

4) Nice easy-listening music.

5) A character generator (one that either attaches to your video camera or by computer) or, as a last resort, hand-made titles.

Price to Charge

Here is a formula for a fair price to charge (you may deduct 20% off for family or friends, but for heavens sake don't do it free). Charge a one-time set-up fee for the first blank tape and the first 20 photos. Charge $4.50 for each additional 20 photos. Charge $15 an hour for adding music. Charge nothing for titles, if they keep it simple like a main title and four or five subtitles, or charge $1 per title until the character generator is paid for. The storage case is free. Buy a nice case (about $.50 to $1.00). Type in the title. Do not write the title and put it in the cheap sleeve that the video tape came in. It looks unprofessional and very trashy. Unless you have a video tape sample of your work, I would not ask for a deposit on the work, and would tell the customer that if they don't like it, they don't pay. Of course, you do not give them the video tape, and never let them keep it for a day to preview. Just play sections for them until they are satisfied that it is a good job.

How to Transfer Photos

Put your video camera on your tripod and hook it up to your TV set or monitor/receiver so you can monitor the transfer. This works a lot better than watching through the eyepiece of your video camera. Next, set the video camera by the edge of a table or desk (the edge of a table works best). Put your video tape in and put in your main title with your Character Generator. A title like "The Smith Family Album" usually works best. You may also want to include your name and phone number before the title for future orders from friends or relatives that may see the tape. Next, put in the first subtitle "1945 to 1947" or "Summer at the Beach", etc. Now, take the first photo and place it on the table.

Set your Video Camera vertically with the lens about an inch from the photo. Put your Video Camera in the Macro mode. This is done by putting the auto-focus on manual and then pushing or pulling on the macro button located on the lens housing (see your owner's manual for exact procedure). Manually turn it left or right until the picture is in focus. Next, raise or lower the Video Camera with your tripod until you get as much of the picture in as possible. At this point you may need to refocus. Also, you may need to add light from a table lamp or other source. Since VCRs record a square picture and photos are horizontal or vertical you will not be able to get the whole picture in unless you use a Special Effects Generator (about $450) or show the outer edges of the photo. But, you will get over 90% of the photo and most, if not all, of the action.

When this is done and it looks good and in focus on your TV or monitor/receiver, you are ready to film. Play back your titles (remember your standard tape setup). When you get to the last title at the front of the tape, count 12 seconds and put the unit on pause. Set the unit on Record Pause. Take the unit off Record Pause by pressing the start button or Record Pause button located on the hand grip of your Video Camera or Camcorder. Count about 10 seconds for each photograph. With this time count you can put about 700 photos on one video tape. Always record in the SP or two-hour mode. Put the unit back on Record

Pause after the 10 seconds and change photos. Now you are ready to go again.

Note: you cannot keep most Video Cameras in Record Pause mode for more than 4 minutes without the unit automatically shutting itself off. So you better hurry or you will have to set up the Record Pause process over again from where you left off.

Continue this process until all titles and photos have been put onto the video tape. Put a nice "The End" title on and then do an audio dub with music. (See HOW TO ADD MUSIC section). Put it in it's nice case and you are done (except to collect your money).

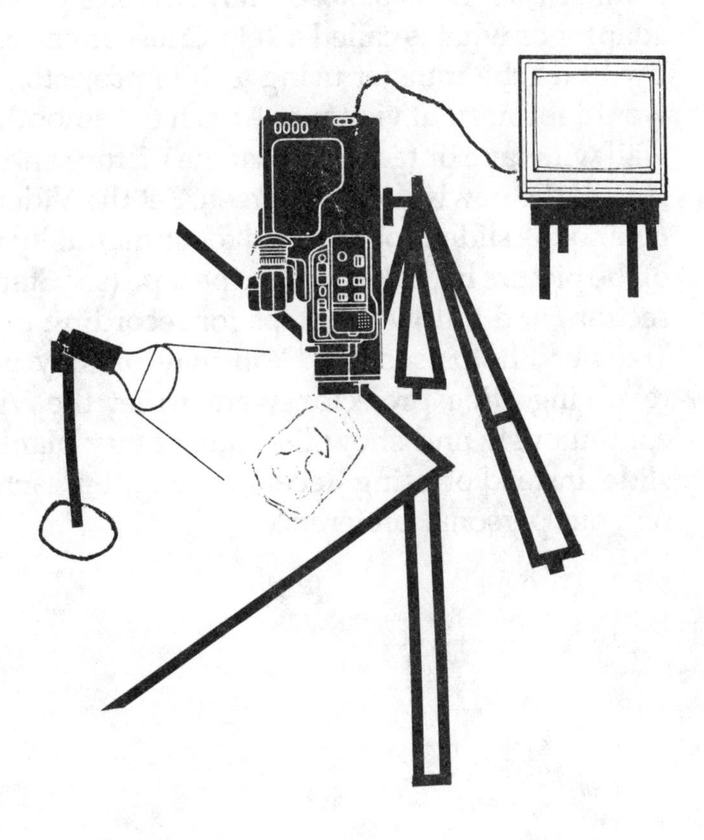

HOW TO TRANSFER SLIDES

Equipment needed:
The equipment needed here is much the same as for transferring photos, plus either a slide projector or a Video Camera slide adapter. Also, a large 11"x14" or 16"x20" piece of smooth, white paper or thicker stock.

Price to charge:
Same as for transferring photos.

How to transfer slides:
The process is almost the same as in transferring photos except a little easier. It is not absolutely necessary that you have a slide adaptor or what is called a Tele-Cina converter. It is your choice. If you do the transfer using a slide projector, set it up like you would for normal viewing. Attach the smooth, white paper to a wall with tape or tacks. Adjust the picture and focus to fill about 90% of the newly-formed screen. Set the Video Camera directly behind the slide projector and focus manually until you get most of the picture in. Take your stripe tape (see Standard Tape Set-up section) and follow the steps for recording photos (see How to Transfer Photos section). You may or may not, when using a revolving slide projector, want to let the Video Camera run continuously and show the momentary blank space after each slide, instead of using Record Pause after each slide. It depends on your personal preference.

HOW TO TRANSFER 8MM, SUPER 8MM, OR 16MM FILM ONTO VIDEO TAPE (The Old to the New Section)

Equipment Needed
The equipment needed is much the same as transferring slides, with the exception that you will need an 8mm, Super 8mm or 16mm projector with an adjustable speed control. This is very important.

Price to Charge for 8mm or Super 8mm
The price should be as follows: $25 set-up fee (includes first blank tape plus 200 feet of film). Then charge $19 for each additional 400 feet. You may break the pricing down into smaller increments if you wish. For instance, if your client has 600 additional feet, charge him $28.50 extra, etc. Here's the catch with 8mm and Super 8mm. If you look at the film box, it may say something like 25 feet. This is because you filmed on one side, turned it over and filmed on the other side. However, when it is processed, the developer will cut the film and splice it together to make 50 feet, so you should charge your client for 50 feet.

Price To Charge For 16mm Film
$35 set-up fee. This includes the first blank tape and the first 200 feet of film. Then charge $24.50 for each additional 400 feet. This is due primarily to the fact that a 16mm projector will cost more than an 8mm or Super 8mm projector.

Warning: Do not attempt to transfer nitrate-based 16mm film (usually made before 1945). If you are not sure, smell the film. Nitrate-based film usually has a pungent odor. Leave this film to the professionals who know how to deal with it. You will see this warning again at the end of this section.

In transferring movie film onto video, set up your equipment as you would for slides, with the Video Camera behind the projector. Set the projector on a smaller object, like a coffee table, as a film projector is taller than a slide projector. The secret to a good film-to-video transfer is speed. If you do not adjust the speed of the moving film you will probably get a flicker, or what looks like light bars, moving progressively up the TV when you play back the video tape. Film and video run at two separate speeds so you have to speed up the film to get rid of the light bars or flicker. Don't worry about any adverse effects created in the viewing by the speeded up film. Grandma will not be running 90 miles an hour. You won't even notice it. Follow the rest of the procedures for filming that are in the TRANSFERRING PHOTOS section. Always hook up your Video Camera to a TV or monitor/receiver to monitor what you're doing. Once again, never attempt to make a transfer of nitrate based 16mm film. Smell the film if you are not sure, and look for a pungent odor. If you are in doubt, take it to a professional.

HOW TO MAKE A VIDEO WILL
(Dead But Not Forgotten)

Equipment Needed
A video camera or Camcorder equipped with a date and time function (this is a legal must) and a tripod.

Price to charge
$75 if the will takes an hour or less; $20 per hour after the first hour.

Step-by-step
There are two reasons to make a video will.

1) It is a legal means to handle your clients estate. You must however encode a date and time on your video tape to make it valid.

2) It gives your client the ability to talk to his/her family and friends that he/she leaves behind.

I have done several video wills with people that have children. These are generally set up in sections. For example:

1) Reading of the will.

2) When the children are 12 years old.

3) When the children are 18 years old.

4) When the children are 21 years old.

They include their hopes and dreams for their children, on a one-on-one basis. This may seem a freak of modern technology, but just think about it a minute. If given the choice between dying suddenly and missing a final farewell, or to die and be able to spend a day or two to have these talks, which would you choose?

You start the video will the same way as your standard tape set-up. You may also want to include, on the front of the video, who is to watch the video. Then, with the year, date and time being encoded on the video tape, have the person introduce themselves with full name, current address, and social security number. Next, have them dispel all other video or written wills that now exist. Next, have the person say the year, date and time so as to back up what is being encoded on the video tape. At no time, from start to finish, should you stop the video camera or Camcorder. You may *not* edit out mistakes or anything else. This would invalidate it as a legal document. Keep this in mind before you start. You may want your client to make a list of things to talk about before starting. At the end of the video will, have your client state that it is the end and nothing else should be added. Make sure that you put the video tape in a case and have your client put it immediately in either a safe deposit box or turn it over to his lawyer or executor of his or her estate.

EDITOR'S NOTE: Please check with your lawyer before filming as a video will may not be valid in your area.

HOW TO VIDEOTAPE A WEDDING (With This Video Section)

Equipment Needed

Video camera or Camcorder with audio dubbing capability, tripod, wedding music.

Price to Charge

$365, including transportation to wedding and reception (limited to 50 miles round trip), and up to four hours of filming (wedding and reception combined); $25 per hour for each additional hour over four.

Step-by-Step

There is nothing better than a wedding on video tape. You get all the movement, vows being said, and sounds that can never be captured on still photos. But, of all of the wedding videos that I've seen, over 95% were so bad that the family member, friend, or so called professional, should be sued or shot. This is one of the types of filming that cannot be redone. You only get one try at it. So, do not attempt this type of video filming unless you feel confident and competent with your equipment. Remember, "if you can't stand the heat, stay out from behind the camera". For all you people out there that would consider renting a video camera and letting your Uncle Fred, or neighbor Bill, film your wedding, let me ask you this. Would you let your Uncle Fred, or neighbor Bill, take still photos of your wedding? Enough said.

If you're going to film a wedding, do it right. First, ask the bride and groom for about 10 or 12 photos each, from the time they were born till the present. Then get about four photos of them together before the present. Put these on the front of the video tape after the main title. Remember to use the maiden name of the bride to be until after the wedding, when her name will change to her married name.

On the day of the wedding, take an outside shot and some inside shots of the church with your video camera or Camcorder. Then, do a short interview with the bride and groom. Also, at this time, remind them to speak up. It has been my experience that in almost every wedding the bride and groom will say the first two words at a normal volume and then almost whisper everything else. Also, at this time, make sure you tell the Maid of Honor, Best Man, and Bridesmaids, not to block the video camera. The best angle to film from (see illustration) is to be on the left-hand side as you face the alter. (see illustration). Do not film from any sacred areas. Check with the church before you set up. Normally you do not need to film everyone being ushered in. This takes up an enormous amount of video tape each time. You will have plenty of time to film who is there during the ceremony. Here are a list of ethical Do's and Don'ts when filming a wedding.

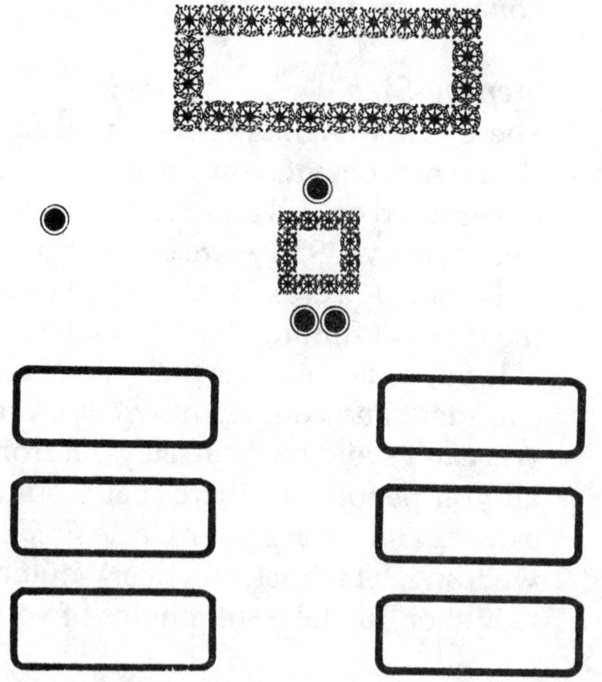

1) Do not move your tripod around. This will distract and interfere with the wedding. Use your zoom instead.

2) Do not use lights. Have them (if necessary) turn up the lights in the church. Extra lighting is a very big distraction.

When filming the wedding make sure that you zoom in on the ring ceremony.

After the entire ceremony has been completed it is not necessary to film everyone leaving. Just the bride and groom, and maybe the parents, as you fade out the scene.

Next, is a neat section which I call video-togrophy. When the regular photographer is taking his or her photos of the bride and groom you can be filming little shots between them. You must be quick to get these shots. Always make sure that the still photographer is not in the scene and that you do not get in his way. If you couldn't get a good shot of the ring ceremony, now is your chance. When this is over you may want to put in a title or leave a space to put one in later (you can only do this if you have a video camera with video and audio insert editing). Use something like "Congratulations, Mr. & Mrs. Smith. Now, go on to the reception.

At the reception, assuming that you drove fast to beat the mob before they converged on the food, film the wonderful food and then the cake. Be creative. Then, film the crowd. Make sure that they are not eating or drinking. There is no better way to ruin your video than showing Uncle Fred with a can of beer in his hands. Next, film the people (section by section) around the tables. This may take two or three set-ups to get everyone in. Again make sure that when you film them, they are not eating or drinking.

Mill around a while, but don't film all the time. About five minutes is plenty. Next, film the following:

1) Toasts

2) Cake cutting

3) First dance

4) Join in dance

5) Throwing the bouquet

6) Taking off and throwing the garter

7) Putting the garter on the one who caught the bouquet, done by the person who caught the garter (if applicable).

Then as a good closing, film the presents and the bride and groom waving.

As a professional, your work begins here. Here's where we do the audio dubs and where to add them.

1) Dub music from the main title through the still pictures of the bride and groom to be, through the shots of the outside and inside of the church, right up to the interviews. Refer to your camera's audio dubbing section for your video camera's particular audio dubbing instructions or check the section on Adding Music in this book.

2) Dub in more music after the ceremony, during the videography session, through the filming of the food, cake and people, right up to the first Toast. This is done because the voices in these sections will be quite noisy and hard to understand anyway.

3) Dub in more music after the putting on of the garter, through to the closing titles.

Pick music for your dubbing that is either of the wedding type or soft selections picked by the bride and groom. If they ordered extra copies make them now.

I used to finish the wedding, go back to my studio, finish the audio dub and be ready to show the finished product by the next morning. By doing this, the sales of copies more than tripled, usually because the out-of-town guests were still in town to see it. Also it brought all kinds of other business because it looked great and was done in record time. Good luck!

Adding music can be done on sight or in your car or van, with the use of a portable cassette or CD player. There is usually a party after the reception and you can present the video there.

This procedure has won me awards and critical acclaim from several Bridal Shops.

HOW TO VIDEOTAPE BIRTHS

Equipment Needed
A video camera or Camcorder (it is helpful to have one with date and time function) and a tripod.

Price to Charge
Usually $100 to $150 if the event does not last over three hours. Also, depending on what time of day or night. If it's before 5am you know to use the $150 charge. Work this out in advance with your client, so that he/she knows that an early morning birth will cost more and he/she isn't surprised with the extra charge.

Step-by-Step
Do your standard tape set-up in advance, since you are on call and may not have time later. Interview your clients and put them at ease. If you have a woman on staff you may want to use her. Try to use the lighting that is available and not use extra spotlights if at all possible as extra lights will bun the baby's eyes. Always act and conduct yourself as a professional. Do not make any copies unless requested to do so by the new parents themselves. You can (and should be) sued for showing any part of a birth to anyone else. Here are some pointers:

1) Try to film the monitor which displays the heartbeat of the mother and baby.

2) Stay out of the doctor's way!! Use your zoom.

3) You may want to use manual focus as the doctor will be between you and the baby. This will cut down on the times that the video camera has to switch its auto zoom from one depth of field to another.

After the filming is done you may want to suggest that your client keep the video tape in a safety deposit box until the child is eighteen and decides for him or herself to see it.

Give the client the tape on the spot unless they want copies, and don't forget to grab the cigar on the way out.

HOW TO VIDEOTAPE A HOUSE FOR INSURANCE PURPOSES

Equipment Needed

Video camera or Camcorder with macro settings.

Price to Charge

For an average-size, three-bedroom house, charge $75 if you can do it in about an hour; $20 per hour for each additional hour.

Step-by-Step

First stripe the videotape as usual (see the section on Striping Tapes), then put down the date that you did the recording on the front of the tape. Use the full date, month, day and year. Put this also on the back of the tape when finished.

When you video tape the house, start in one corner of each room and pan the entire room slowly, including drapes, wallpaper, etc. Do not forget closets or bookshelves (get the titles of books on video tape). Film light fixtures, towels, everything. Ask if there have been any improvements made on the house. A good example would be additions to a small bathroom; a wooden towel bar ($35), a wood or brass medicine cabinet ($100 to $250) or even a wooden toilet seat ($50). Don't laugh, it all adds up.

Do the garage and/or storage shed. Tools are not cheap. When you're finished, make sure your client takes the video tape to either another relative, or to a safety deposit box, for safekeeping. Believe me, if something happens, like a fire, they will get a lot more money from the insurance company than if all they had were a couple of photos of their TV or stereo.

If items have serial numbers, use your macro setting to record them. Also, don't forget jewelry or antiques. Ask how much it is worth, not how much they paid for it.

You can ask the owner to talk into the microphone about these things as you go along.

At this time I would like to relate what happened to me personally on November 5, 1990. I was robbed. They took approximately $16,000 worth of things including my Camcorders, VCRs, SEG, computer, etc. None of the stuff was used in my writing, just personal "video nut" stuff. Anyway, a representative of my insurance company (both the company and the representative shall remain nameless) made two statements to me, which shocked me into relaying them to you, in case it happens to you. The first was, the representative stated that a time-dated video tape from a bonded, licensed videographer (myself) would be no good to prove that I had the stuff. The manager of the company (after I conferred with the courthouse, my lawyer, and requested a new representative) said that it was valid. Ladies and gentlemen, a time-dated video tape or your house is valid in all 50 states. To be on the safe side in Canada, please check with your insurance agent or lawyer before you film.

The second thing that the first representative said to me was that, because I used my Camcorder to record the contents of my house, it was used for a business purpose, so the Camcorder that was used should be considered business and disallowed. Is this a catch 22 or what? That too was turned around and the claim was finally settled (after many sworn statements and over two months later). To make a very long story short, I was finally paid and I am off the insurance company's Christmas list. I've also now taken a policy with State Farm Insurance which is where I should have gotten it in the first place. (I am from the U.S.A.)

So, if an insurance company tries to treat you like you just fell off the turnip truck, and you only used your Camcorder and other video equipment for personal things or as a hobby, your Camcorder should be covered on your home policy. But if you do use your Camcorder for business such as videography, get some business insurance for your equipment.

INTERVIEWING FOR MONEY (One Video is Worth 10,000 Photos)

Equipment Needed:
Video camera, tripod and, if you are doing the interview yourself, a remote pause button for the Camcorder.

Price to Charge:
A good fee is $65 for the first hour (assuming it will take you 1/2 hour to set up and prepare). Then charge $25 for each additional 1/2 hour.

Doing the Interview:
First, do your normal videotape stripe. Second, if you have a blinking red tally light on the front of the Camcorder, COVER IT UP! It is very distracting to the interviewee. Next, build into the interview today's date and what date you are talking about. Just mention the dates as you progress in time. Most of the time you will be interviewing older people so it is good to explain what you are doing so they will be at ease. (Don't assume they know about video.) Try starting with what they remember about their childhood, for instance, did they buy or bake their bread? Did they have electricity or an outhouse? (Some of the funniest stories I've heard are about outhouses or how they got water into their house.)

Next, ask them about their grandparents' accomplishments or what country they were from, etc. Some more examples are:

- Did you have a good childhood?
- What kind of games did you play?
- What did you do at parties?
- What did you want to be when you grew up?
- Did you achieve what you planned?

- What would you hope for your children or grandchildren?

These are just some guidelines. You may also want to get a professional guide specific to this subject. The best I've seen is put out by:

Living Family Albums
6200 Savoy Drive, Suite 440
Houston, TX 77036

IDENT-A-KID (Every Six Months)

Equipment Needed
Video camera or Camcorder (hopefully with date encoding capability) with macro and a tripod.

Price to Charge
If you have your own store front or office where the client can come to you, I do not feel that you should charge anything if your client supplies you with the video tape, or, just the cost of the video tape, if he doesn't. If you do not have your own store front or office and you have to go to your client, you should charge a small amount for gas and travel time. The reason I suggested to not charge for this service is because our youth of today is our future of tomorrow and should be protected at any cost. You may even want to advertise this in a local newspaper.

Step-by-Step
1) Set-up a video tape as usual.

2) Put in the child's name, date of birth, the date you are filming, color of eyes, hair, and blood type. Have a measuring stick attached to the wall and have the child stand by it.

3) Do a full shot, then zoom up to the face. Have the child smile. Have the child turn sideways, then smile.

4) Have the child show his or her other side then smile.

5) Ask the mother or father if the child has any unusual markings or scars. Film them close up with the macro setting on your camera.

6) If the child has had his/her ears pierced, film them with and without an earring in. This is for later identification purposes.

7) Have the child speak. This is for possible voice print identification purposes. The macro setting on your camera can also be used for fingerprint identification. Just have the child put his/her hand on an inkpad and then film, using the macro focus of your video camera or Camcorder.

This procedure should be done every six months, at least until the age of 18, and then your client should have it done once a year.

TRANSFERRING IMPORTANT DOCUMENTS

Equipment Needed
Same as for transferring photos.

Price to Charge
The price to charge for transferring important documents is much the same as with photos with the exception that you should charge by the shot rather than the document. For example, if you are video taping a long legal document you may need to start and stop the Video Camera three times or more to get all of the document in, piece by piece. So, charge by the shot.

Transferring Documents
The procedure is virtually the same as with transferring photos. Make sure when you do this that you get all of the important papers such as birth certificates, stocks, bonds, etc. Also, make sure that your client puts the finished video tape in a safety deposit box, or in a place other than where the important documents are. You may also want to put a date and/or time code on the tape.

BUSINESS VIDEOS (Dawn of a New Age)

If You Use and Send Video Tapes

Gone are the days where a black-and-white Xerox copy of a flyer will get lots of business for your company. Gone are the days of your color brochure ending up in the circular file (trash can) before it got anywhere near the intended readers. Gone are the days of spending thousands of dollars to redo catalogs just to add a few new products to them and then having them end up where the color brochure did. Here are just some of the uses of video today.

It's hard to be in two places at once. Many businesses record their important meetings and distribute them to the other branches. This is a cost-effective way to have their new policies heard by all of their employees.

For demonstration of new techniques, training, or procedures, nothing beats video. It's a sales tool that is light years ahead of the competition.

Instead of sending out a catalog, send out a video of your products. To customers it is like seeing the product first hand. I have never heard of a company throwing a video into the trash can without seeing it first. People are curious.

Video tapes are important. They show that your company is not in the stone age, that your company is moving forward, not backward. That's where the people you want to do business with want you to be.

VIDEO NEWSHOUND (or How to Sniff Out Money Section)

At first, you may think that you can't videotape anything with good enough quality to be put on TV. Think again. At least twice a week on the news I see videos described by the newsman as "taken by an amateur videographer". Example: Recently, I saw film of a helicopter putting an air conditioning unit on top of a building. During this operation, the tail rotor hit something and the helicopter dropped its load and crashed. It was all captured by someone just like you.

Your local news station is now equipped to handle your VHS tapes. So call up your news station or cable company if you think you have something newsworthy, or when you become good with your video camera, and ask to cover small assignments that they might not have the time to cover. This is not how Barbara Walters got started, but I don't think the TV station or cable company will laugh at you if you approach them with the idea these days.

It's just a matter of being in the right place at the right time. It's also fun and you might make a few bucks too.

HOW TO USE THE ZOOM
(The Closer You Get Section)
or (Let's Play Leap-frog)

With the advent of modern technology, all Camcorders (except the cheapest of the lot), (I know I'm not supposed to say cheapest, but least expensive. But, in video, I think cheapest applies well) have power zoom, usually six to one, eight to one, or ten to one (not including digital zoom).

You should not use the zoom for more than half of its capability without it being on a tripod or shoulder brace. The more you use the zoom, the slower you should pan or move the camera also.

Especially, do not walk with the Camcorder. There are two reasons for this. First, if you walk, the natural movement of your body will give you an up and down movement, which will transfer to the tape you are making. Second, you won't be able to see where you are putting your feet. (Even the EIS [Electronic Image Stabilizer] system won't help you if you trip over something.)

I suggest that you use what I call the Leap-frog tactic. First, place your feet straight forward about 12 to 14 inches apart. Then zoom out on your subject. If you can't go close enough, stop the camera, walk closer and then place your feet again and start your zoom over. This will give you a better picture than walking up to your subject with the zoom out.

HOW TO USE THE MACRO LENS
(Incredible Closeness)

I love using the macro. Especially when I sell Camcorders. I will take a dollar bill and put it right on the lens while using the macro lens and show people both sides of the dollar bill at the same time, in perfect focus.

Focusing with the macro lens is done manually even if you have auto-focus on your Camcorder. The macro setting is located on the right side of the focusing ring as you face the Camcorder. To operate it, push or pull the release mechanism (button) and slowly move it toward the bottom of the Camcorder while looking through the eyepiece. You can get as close as 3/16th of an inch. The macro is used to transfer photos onto video tape or to shoot any small object such as flowers, butterflies, stamps, coins, etc.

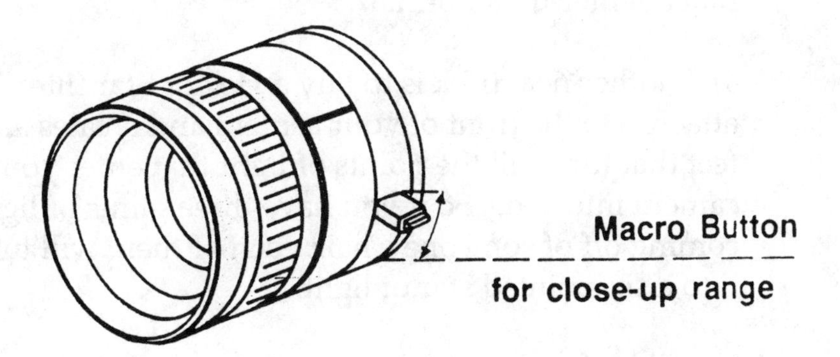

SPECIAL EFFECTS (Beyond Reality)

If you have done any type of special effects with a still camera, almost all of them can be applied to your video camera.

1) If you put Vaseline around the edges of the lens it will create a dreamlike effect. Don't put this directly on your lens, but put it on your haze filter. Of course, the Vaseline can be taken off with very soft tissues or a lens cleaning kit. Don't submerge your whole camera to clean it. This could result in damage to your camera. (No joke. You have to tell some people about this.)

2) Using dry ice gives a fog-like effect. You would be surprised at the incredible effect that five dollars worth of dry ice at a wedding will create.

3) If you are filming a small object on the ground, try getting flush with ground to make the object appear much larger than normal.

4) Another neat trick is to buy a Hex or Star filter. This attaches to the front of your camera and creates an effect that turns all the points of light that enter your camera into stars. So if you have three glints of light coming off of someone's hair, each of them will turn into a six-pointed star of light.

5) Still by far, the best special effects are done with digital, right in your camera. You need to buy either a digital Camcorder or add digital from a digital VCR or Special Effects Generator, in order to take advantage of these.

DEW INDICATOR (From the Frying Pan Into the Fire Section)

The Dew Indicator is a device built into deck units or Camcorders to protect the equipment from excessive moisture buildup on the video heads. Going from an air-conditioned car to a very hot outdoors, or going from the very cold outside to a warm room, or putting a cold video tape into a VCR or Camcorder, will create dew or moisture.

The Dew Indicator will automatically shut the unit down, usually from about a half hour to an hour. Do not attempt to operate the unit until the Dew light goes out.

Always try to acclimatize the deck, Camcorder, or video tape, to the new environment before use. This will avoid a lot of disappointment.

TIPS ON FILMING
(Icing on the Cake Section)

1) Try to film with the sun or light source behind you. Otherwise the subject you are filming will look darker than the background.

2) Try to use a tripod whenever possible (especially when using your zoom capability).

3) Make sure your equipment and video tapes have a chance to warm up or cool down, to meet conditions of the new environment, before use. (See Dew Indicator Section).

4) Never walk with a Camcorder.

5) Make sure that you carry twice the batteries that you think you will need (especially if it is a hot day or if you are going to turn the equipment on and off a lot).

6) Never chew gum and use a Camcorder. (Just checking to see if you were paying attention.)

7) Never point the video equipment towards the sun even when the Camcorder is off.

8) Always use a haze filter. (See the "Must Have" Accessory Section.) Also, put the lens cap on the camera whenever it is not in use to protect the lens.

9) Avoid using colors like red or blue as backgrounds or clothes. They tend not to come out as well as you would want. Also, avoid small pin stripes as they have a tendency to give a wavy effect.

SHOULD I CLEAN MY VIDEO HEADS (Age Old Question Section)

Of all the questions ever asked about VCRs, this one is on the top of the list. In almost every VCR magazine there is an article about cleaning your heads or not cleaning your heads. On the pro-clean side the experts tend to agree that, because most people buy inexpensive blank video tapes, and they do not examine a rental tape before they rent it (please see the section on renting video tapes), it is necessary to clean their video heads more than once a year. On the con side the experts say for the same reasons, the customer will buy a cheap head cleaner and that all maintenance should be done by a qualified technician. I'm on the pro side, if and only if, you follow this procedure.

1) You do not put your VCR on top of your TV or within 12 inches of the bottom of your TV. It can, over a period of time, damage the VCR or TV. It would be OK to put your VCR on top of most monitors as they should be shielded.

2) Examine rental tapes before you rent them. Read that section.

3) Do not ever rent a head cleaning cassette or rewind the cassette and use it again. I would recommend that you use it after 60 to 80 hours of playing and/or recording. Notice that I said playing and recording. If I recorded a two-hour movie, and then two half-hour programs, and then, one night sat down and watched everything that I had recorded, some people would say that I had used my machine only 3 hours. Wrong, I used it for six hours. I'm not saying you should keep a minute-by-minute log, just keep a mental note of your playing and recording hours.

4) If you follow the first three steps , you should still also have your VCR and video heads cleaned by a professional, but instead of once a year, you can extend the time to once every year and a

half. I've encountered hundreds of cases where someone has brought me a VCR that wouldn't work. Put it on the counter for service. When I asked them when was the last time the machine was cleaned, they would smile with naivete. "Oh. I've never cleaned it in three years". Like it was something to be proud of. Unlike TVs or stereos, a VCR *does* need special care. Being a video expert I take this personally. To me it's like running a car off a cliff and then telling a mechanic that there might be something wrong with the front end. On the positive side, if you follow this guide, your VCR will last two to three times longer than the same VCR without this type of care.

5) When getting your VCR heads cleaned, have it done by a professional. Out of 35 video rental places that advertised that they cleaned video heads and machines, I would only recommend two. And they sent their's out to be cleaned. Out of the other 33, not one employed personnel with more than four hours training on VCR repair or cleaning. Not one had a VCR belt in stock or knew how to replace one. Not one knew where or how to replace internal fuses. These are the three most common problems of VCRs. So, ask for training credentials.

6) A video cleaning system should be able to clean the following:

Back Tension Arm: The back tension arm applies constant tension at the beginning of the tape drive. If not clean, the audio is affected. This arm can only be cleaned with the backside of a cleaning ribbon.

Threading Guides: These guides move your video tape on and off the drum at a precise angle and can put lines across the bottom of the screen that can't be removed with the tracking control.

Rotary Drum: This drum carries the video and "Hi-Fi" audio heads. Clean grooves in the drum provide an air bearing effect. Your tape is "sanded" on the drum. The picture jitters. A wet and dry technology is required to thoroughly clean the grooves.

Audio Heads/Control Track Heads: The audio head reads the normal audio signal from the top edge of the tape. A dirty head can muffle or even eliminate the audio. The control track head reads the playback speed signal from the bottom edge of the tape. Dirt here can vary tape speed.

Capstan/Pinch Roller: The true "tape eaters." If not cleaned, dirt on this mechanism is squeezed into your tape. Dirt and excess lubricants are pressed into a ridge line beneath tape on start-up. Your tape is pressed against this ridge and wrinkled. Tape speed variations and/or complete loss of picture are a direct result.

Until recently, I used to recommend Geneva head cleaners. They do a pretty good job on the heads, but the ALLSOP brand cleans the capstan and pinch roller with its unique cleaning system.

VIDEO EDITING

So, you've completed your video taping and you want to add music or insert photos or titling on your video tape. In this section we will cover all the video equipment needed to accomplish this. In each section we will show you ways to edit with or without video and audio insert editing capabilities. Just pick the method that applies to your equipment.

We will also mention different types of SEGs (Special Effects Generators) and different types of CGs (Character Generators). If you're looking to buy a system, the system that you pick is determined by how much money you want to spend and what types of videos you want to produce. Whenever you purchase equipment always ask yourself "What am I going to do with it in the next two years?" Always keep your future needs in mind.

ASSEMBLE EDITING

There are two types of video editing. The most common type is the Assemble Edit. This is done by adding one scene at a time (see Illustration 1).

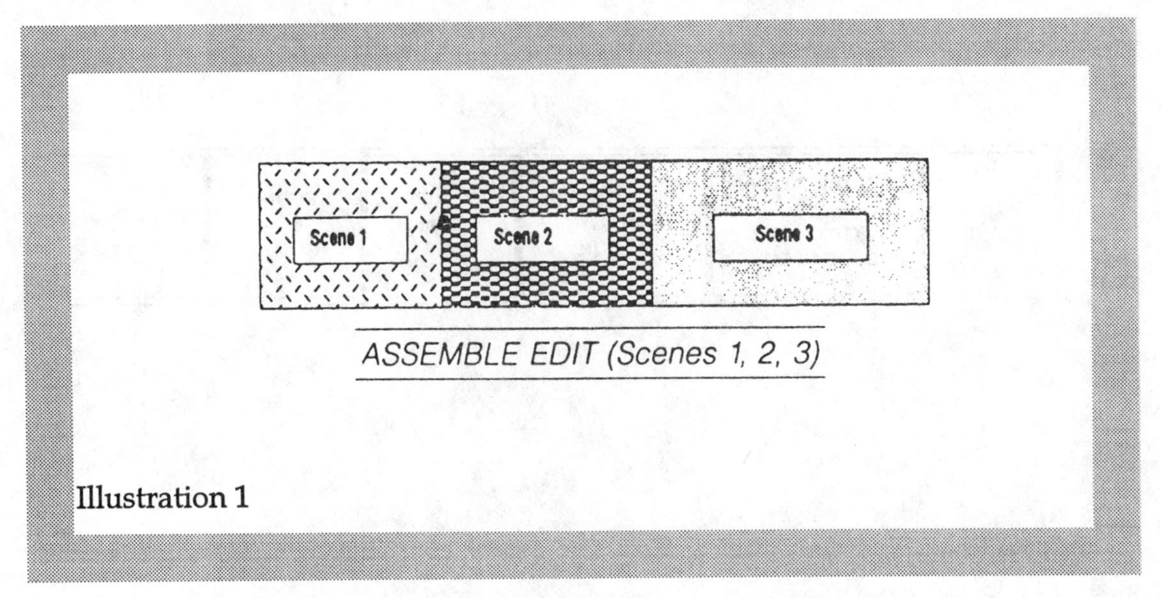

Illustration 1

This is done very easily with your equipment (see Illustration 2).

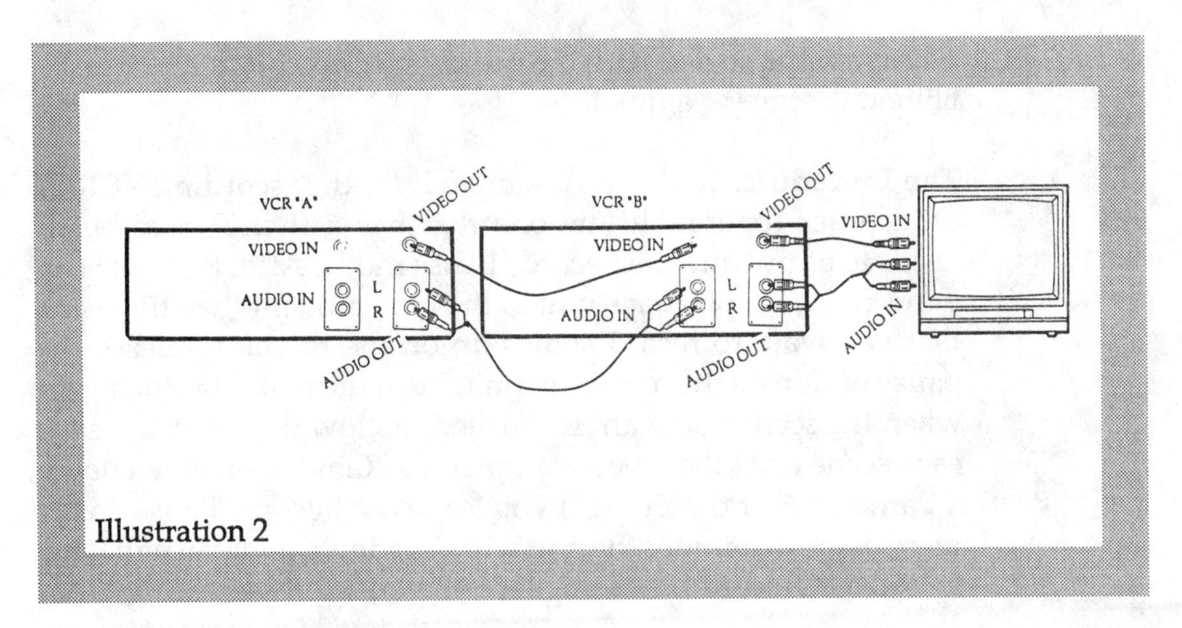

Illustration 2

To eliminate a moiré line (faint color bar squiggling down the screen at the beginning of each scene) you will need to have a flying erase head on the recording VCR or Camcorder.

There is a second way of doing an Assemble Edit. This is done when you are in control of the production. Examples of this would be transferring 8mm movie film, or photos, onto video tape (see Illustration 3).

30 SEC. BLANK	PRODUCTION OF VIDEO ONE PUBLICATIONS	THE SMITH FAMILY ALBUM	FIRST 8mm MOVIE	SECOND 8mm MOVIE	ETC.

Illustration 3

This is accomplished with the use of one Camcorder and assembling one scene at a time.

The Procedure: To do an Assemble Edit, the recording VCR or Camcorder (preferably the one that has a flying erase head) needs to be put into the Record/Pause mode. After this has been done, place the playback unit in the play mode. When the scene that you want to record shows up on the monitor, release the pause button on the recording unit. Push the pause button again when the scene you want is finished. Follow this procedure for each scene until the tape is completed. (Remember, when using a Camcorder or deck unit, if you leave the Record/Pause on for more than 2-5 minutes the unit will shut down and you will have to set the Record/Pause again.) If you are assembling from several video tapes onto one, and will need more than two minutes between assemblings, record about three seconds or so more on the end of the last scene. That way when you set up again you don't have to have split second timing on the Record/Pause button.

Hooking up extra equipment: When doing an Assemble Edit you may want to add an editing controller. This is done by following Illustration 4.

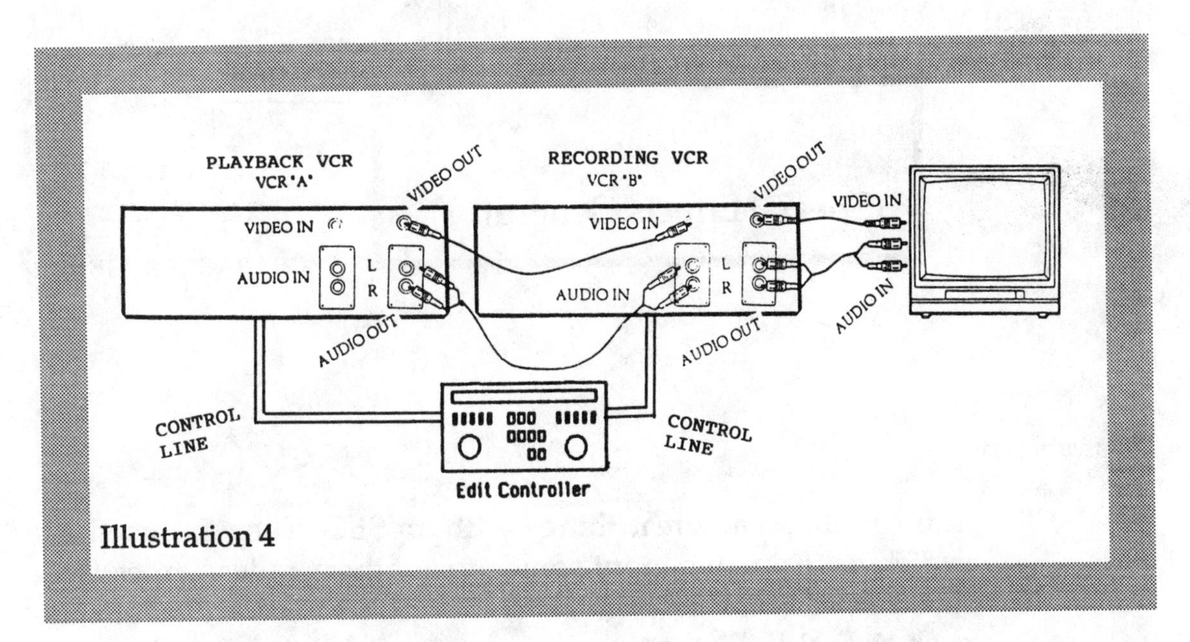

Illustration 4

There is generally no reason to use an editing controller for such things as weddings, graduations, film-to-video transfers, unless you have to have accuracy of 1/30th of a second. In 16 years, I've only had to use an editing controller for TV commercials and music videos.

Now's a great time to hook up an SEG (Special Effects Generator) and a CG (Character Generator). There are several types of SEGs that are available. We have included a whole section on them. The hook up of all of them is very similar. A typical example is found in Illustration 5.

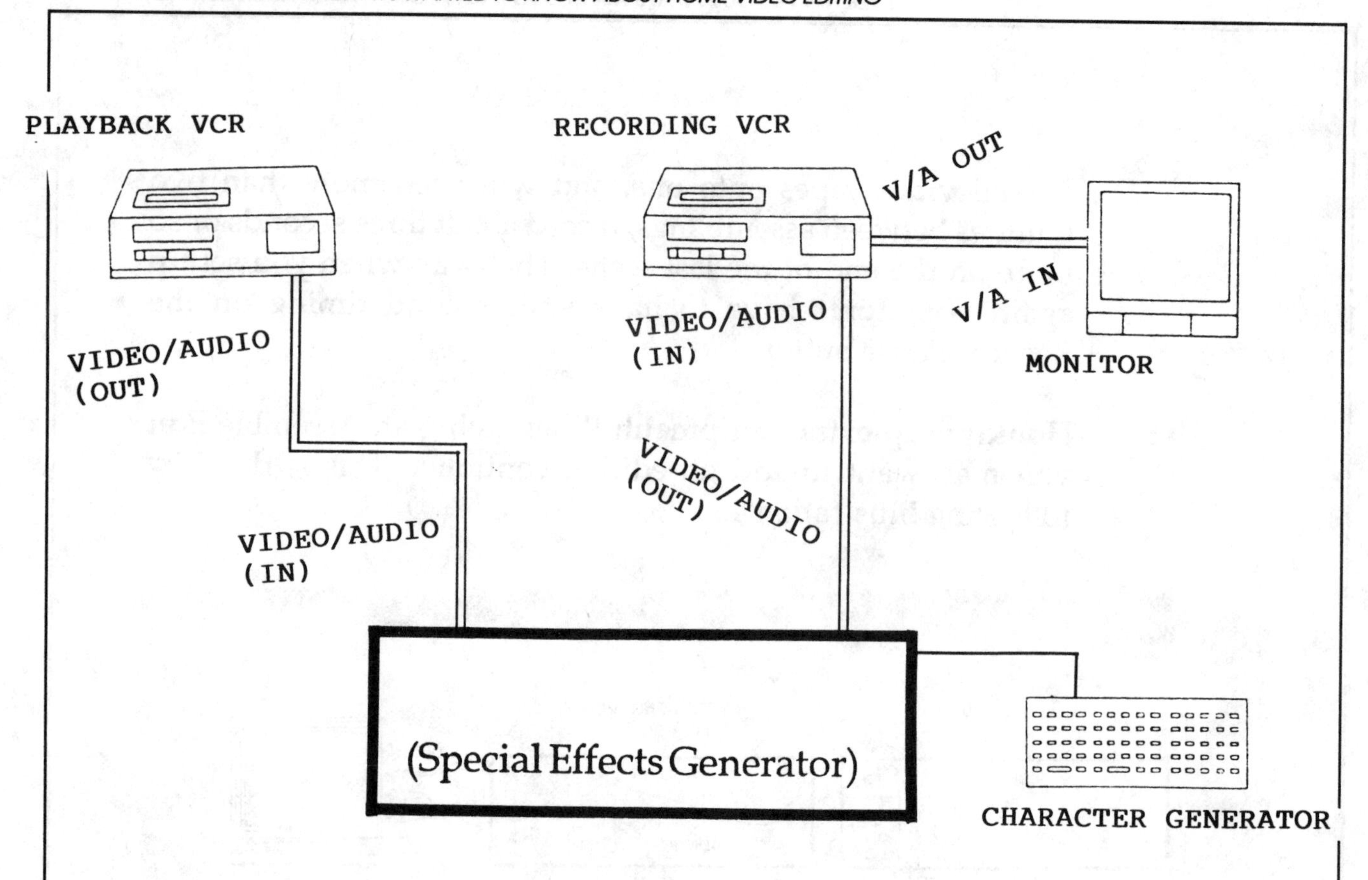

Illustration 5

You can do some great things with an SEG. They are used as switchers (from one input source to another), fades, wipes (see illustration 6 on next page), and cuts. Some have digital effects such as P-N-P (Picture in picture), mosaic, digital painting and stroboscopic.

The patterns or wipes will allow you to put any color where the black shows and wipe over a video picture. Some new SEGs are able to wipe one video input source (Camcorder, computer graphics, VCR) over another without the use of a TBC (Time Base Corrector) like the Panasonic's SEG WJ-AVE5. (They call it a digital AV mixer.) We will tell you more about it in the SEG section of this book.

This is when you would add titles with a CG (Character Generator) if you didn't add them as you were filming.

Illustration 6

You can hook up a CG to your SEG to get an O'GEE (just a joke). Some other SEGs (Newteks, Video-toaster, Videonics, Direct Ed, Direct Ed plus) have CGs built into them. SEGs like the Panasonic WJ-AVE5 and the Shomi Cheetah or the Adventurer can add a CG to them very easily.

In Illustration 7 is a sample of a standard system connection. We will use the Panasonic hook up as an example.

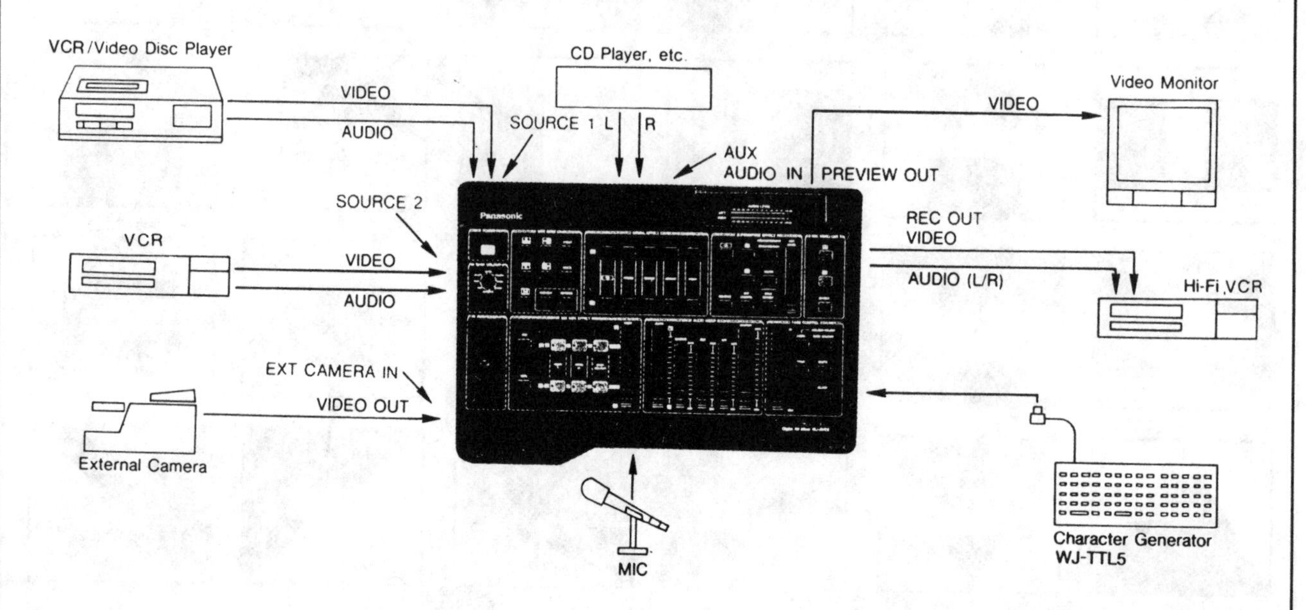

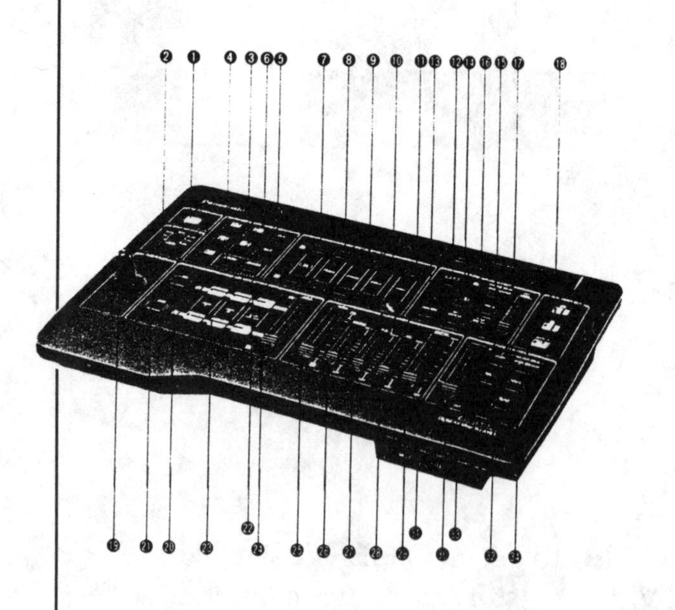

1. Power On/Off Switch
2. Back Color Select Switch
3. Wipe Pattern Select Switch
4. Wipe Direction Select Switch
5. Picture-in-Picture Switch
6. Multi-Wipe Switch
7. Digital Effect On/Off Switch
8. Still (Freeze) Switch
9. Strobe Switch
10. Mosaic Switch
11. Paint Switch
12. Superimpose On/Off Switch
13. Picture/Title Reverse Switch
14. Superimpose Input Select Switch
15. Title Color Select Switch
16. Title Effect Switch (Edging/Shadowing)
17. Title Key Level
18. Recording Video Output Select Switch
19. Joystick Positioner
20. Mix Switch
21. Wipe Switch
22. A-channel Input Select Switch
23. B-channel Input Select Switch
24. Wipe/Mix Lever
25. Audio Input Channel Balance
26. Audio Source Level Control
27. Aux Input Level Control
28. Mic Input Level Control
29. Audio Output Master Level Control
30. Fade Control
31. Mic Input
32. Fade Select Switch (Video/Title)
33. Character Generator Input
34. Fade Color Select Switch

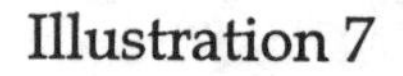

Illustration 7

INSERT EDITING

The second type of editing is called Insert Editing. This procedure is commonly used in music videos or for getting rid of bad scenes between two good scenes. (See Illustration 8).

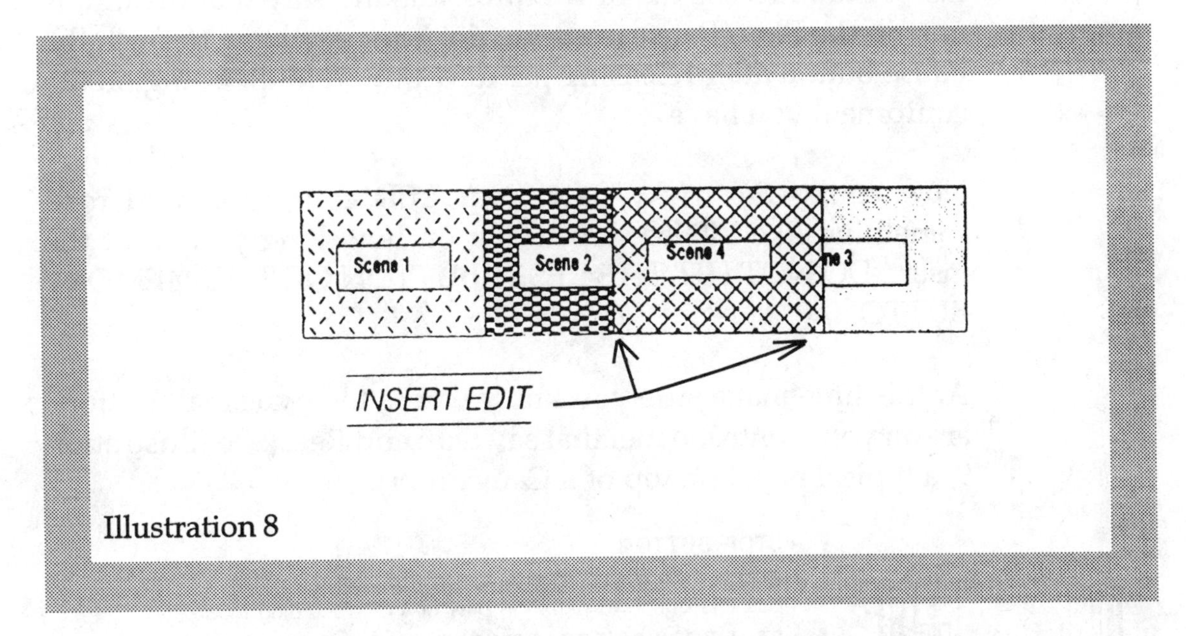

Illustration 8

The equipment hook up is the same for an Insert Edit as it is for an Assemble Edit (see illustration 2 on Assemble Editing).

Procedure: Insert Editing is much harder to perform than an Assemble Edit because you have to worry about both the beginning of the scene and also finishing the end of the scene cleanly. What I mean by cleanly at the end is, if you just stop the machine at the end of the new scene that you inserted (without being in the insert dub mode) it will look very bad at the end for 10 to 15 seconds.

To do a proper Insert Edit, follow this procedure exactly.

On the recording VCR deck (or Camcorder) with Insert Editing capabilities, play the master tape until you get to the end of where you want the new scene. Put the unit on Pause. Push the counter display button, push reset to set the counter to 0000, then push memory so the LED readout will look like M0000. Now push your Rew (Review) button while the unit is still in Play/Pause mode. Look at the monitor or EVF (Electronic View Finder) until you get to the point where you want to start the Insert Edit. Release the Rew button making sure that the unit is now in the Play/Pause mode again. You may have to push the Pause button after releasing the Rew button (depending on the equipment you have).

Now comes the tricky part. Your LED counter should read something like M9965 depending on how long you want the insert. DO NOT HIT THE RESET BUTTON OR THE MEMORY BUTTON.

At this time make sure you know where the two small buttons are on your control panel that say Dub and Rec. (See Illustration 9, a typical panel on top of a Camcorder).

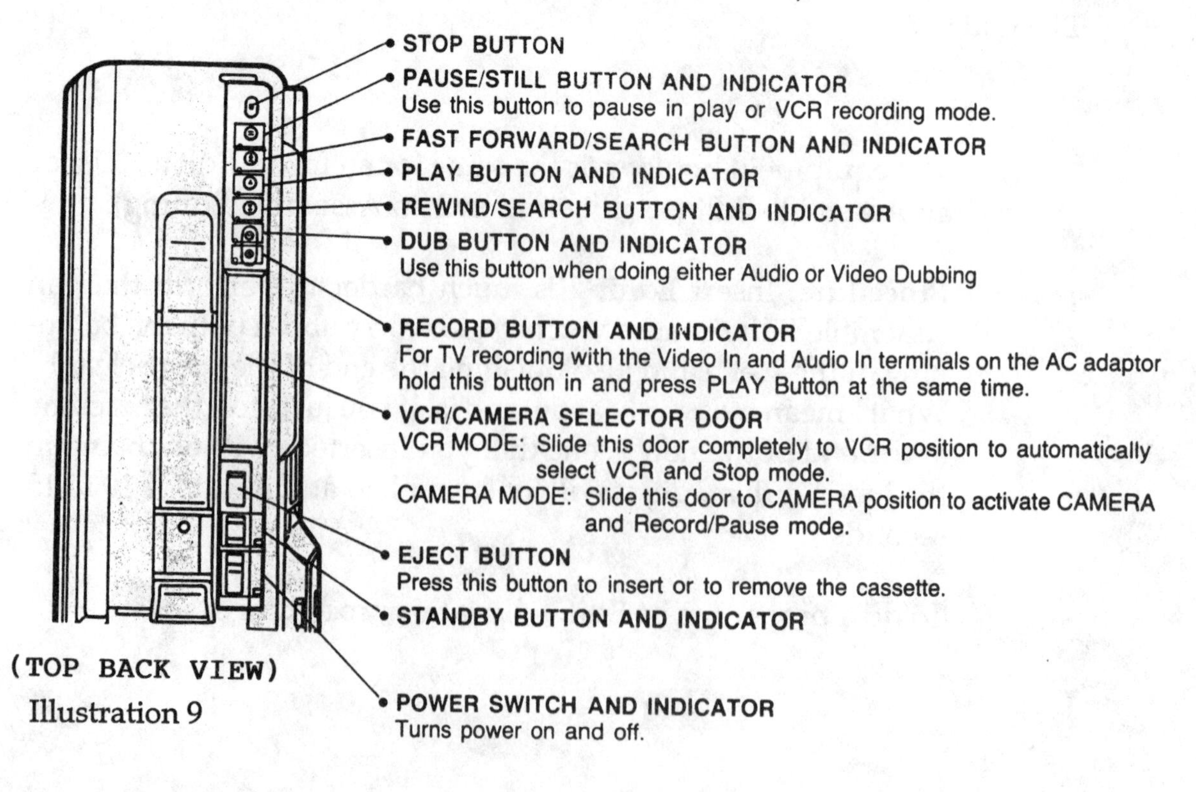

Illustration 9

At the same time push both the Dub and the Rec buttons. You will know if you did this right by looking at the monitor or EVF. There will be no picture on the screen.

On the playback unit push play until you reach the point where you want to insert onto the master. At the end of the insert (when the unit reaches M0000 on the counter) the unit will shut the recording off and put itself back into the Play/Pause mode.

DO NOT MANUALLY push the Pause button or the Stop button until the unit has gone through this cycle. If you do, it will mess up your video insert. Note: When you do a video insert edit it will not affect the audio portion of your master tape. All you did was replace one video scene with another. (A lot of music videos are done this way.)

As in Assemble Editing, you can also add special effects at the same time. To hook up SEGs and CGs refer to Illustration 5 in the Assemble Edit section.

Assemble Editing and Insert Editing are the two hardest things to master. It just takes practice and patience. Keep the Reference Guide handy to help you out.

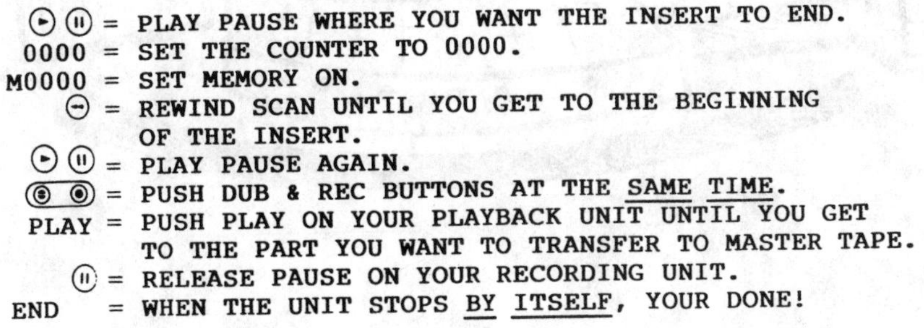

```
       = PLAY PAUSE WHERE YOU WANT THE INSERT TO END.
 0000  = SET THE COUNTER TO 0000.
M0000  = SET MEMORY ON.
       = REWIND SCAN UNTIL YOU GET TO THE BEGINNING
         OF THE INSERT.
       = PLAY PAUSE AGAIN.
       = PUSH DUB & REC BUTTONS AT THE SAME TIME.
 PLAY  = PUSH PLAY ON YOUR PLAYBACK UNIT UNTIL YOU GET
         TO THE PART YOU WANT TO TRANSFER TO MASTER TAPE.
       = RELEASE PAUSE ON YOUR RECORDING UNIT.
 END   = WHEN THE UNIT STOPS BY ITSELF, YOUR DONE!
```

Illustration 10

ADDING MUSIC TO VIDEOS

Adding music to videos is very important. As with feature films today, music accounts for about 40% of the production. A movie like ET has been rumored to have music that is 60% of the production.

ADDING MUSIC AS YOU ARE RECORDING

There are several ways of adding music to a production. The first is as you are doing the filming. This is done with a unit like Cam-Tunes™. It works with all Camcorders equipped with an external microphone jack. An earphone is provided to be used to monitor the mixing from the microphone and the Cam-Tunes™ unit. You connect one end of the unit to the external microphone jack on the Camcorder and attach the unit itself to the accessory shoe of the Camcorder. Put the mini jack into the mini output connection of a portable cassette recorder. Put in a tape (Cam-Tunes™ also has a wide variety of sound effects tapes; i.e. jungle, ocean, etc.) and adjust the mixing control on your Cam-Tunes™ and you are ready to go. Cam-Tunes™ is also great at sporting events. Just tune in on an AM/FM portable radio whatever station is covering the event and Voila! you have blow by blow excitement. You can contact Cam-Tunes™ by writing:

NORBURN Inc.
P.O. Box 62276
Colorado Springs, CO 80920

ADDING MUSIC WITHOUT DUBBING CAPABILITIES

This is done if your Camcorder or deck unit does not have Video/Audio insert capabilities. It has to be done on a copy of the video tape, and not the master.

This is done quite easily (see Illustration 1).

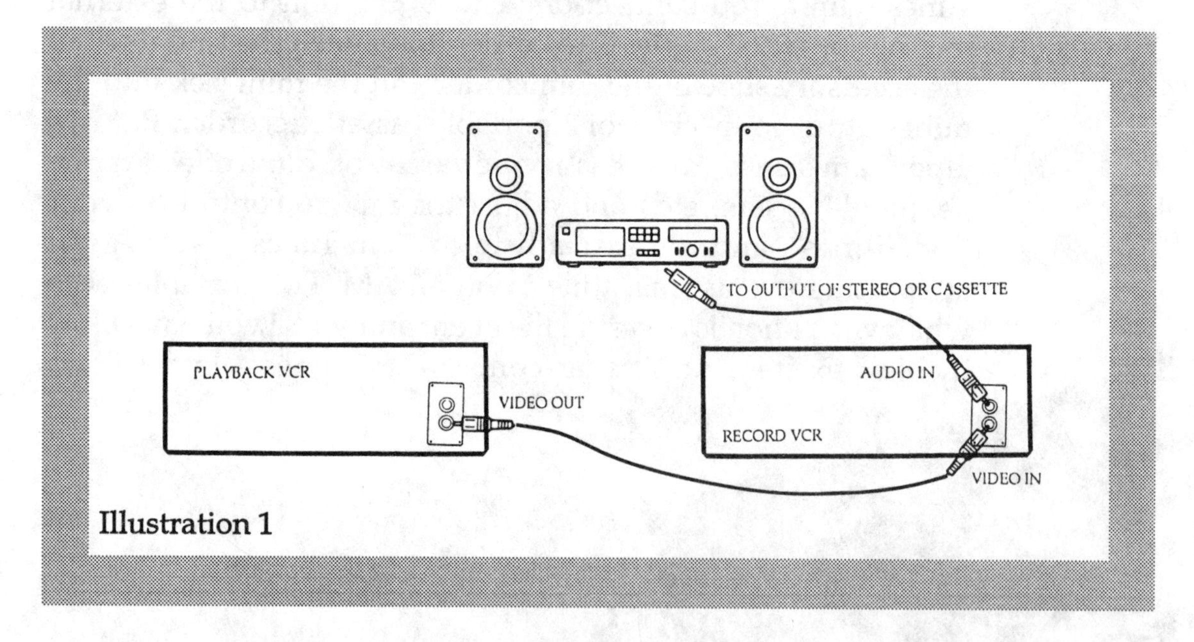

Illustration 1

Run an RCA line out of the first VCR or Camcorder with the master video tape in it to the second (recording) VCR. Next run an RCA line out of your stereo or portable stereo to the audio of your VCR and run lines to your Monitor/Receiver or TV. Push play on the first VCR and record on the second as you start the music on the stereo. This way you are getting the video recorded from the first VCR and the new audio from the stereo.

Adding an Audio Mixer: You can also mix the audio from the master tape and the music from the stereo (see Illustration 2).

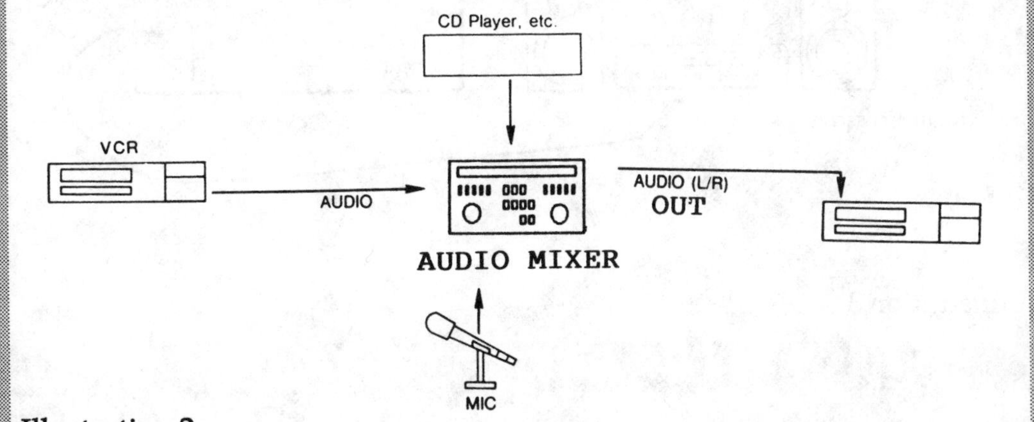

Illustration 2

The procedure is very similar to that in Illustration 1, but you add an audio mixer. If you have a microphone input into your audio mixer you can also mix narration of your video while mixing the audio from the master video and music from your stereo. (See Royalty Free Music Section for your music.)

Adding Music With Audio Dub Capabilities: The third way to add music (and most common) is if your equipment has Video/Audio insert capabilities, because the audio editing is done on the master videotape. (See Illustration 3 on the next page).

Procedure:

1) Put master tape in VCR or Camcorder with audio insert capabilities.

2) Push play on the video until you get to the end of where you want to add music.

3) Set the digital counter to 0000.

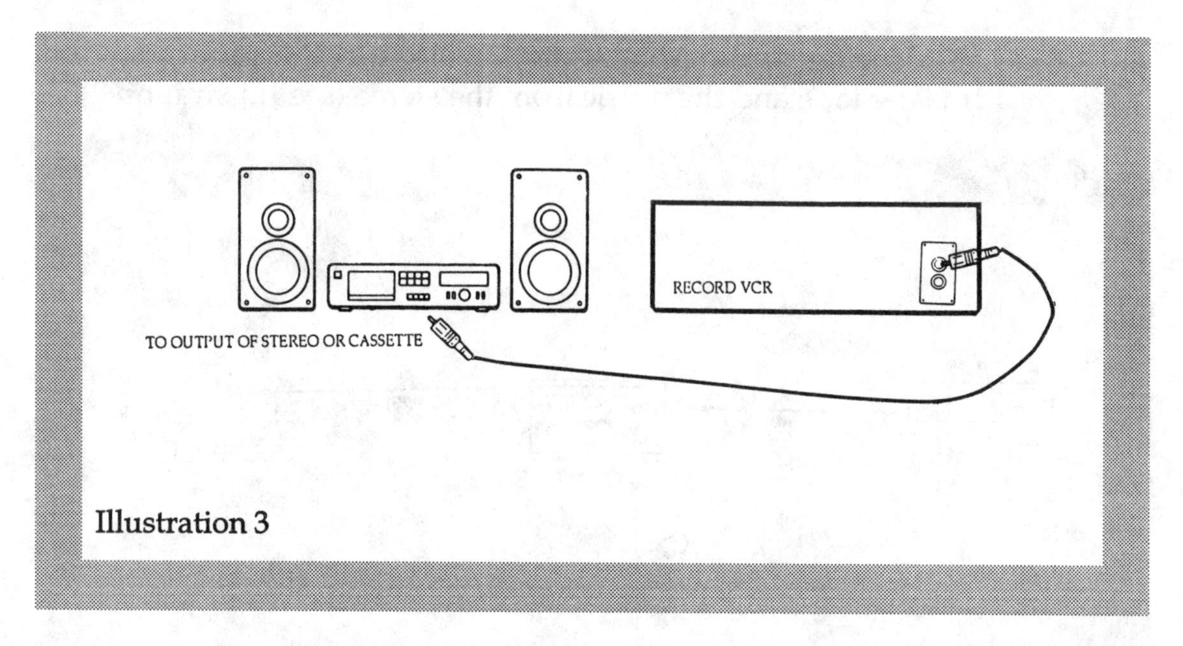

Illustration 3

4) Play/Review the tape back until you get to the beginning of where you want to do the audio dub.

5) Put the unit into the Play/Pause mode.

6) Push the Audio dub button and at the same time push the Play button. This will put the unit into the Dub/Pause mode.

7) Start the music on the stereo.

8) Push the Pause button to start the recording.

9) Push the Pause button again to stop the audio recording when the tape counter reaches 0000. You might want to start fading out the volume at the last 10 counter marks before 0000 for a smoother effect.

You can also add an audio mixer in your recording (see illustration 2).

Caution: You must manually stop the audio dub. Do not put the unit on M0000 as the unit will not stop at 0000 automatically.

DUMMY-PLUG THE MICROPHONE

When you are doing jobs that don't need sound, or you will add sound to later, such as transferring photos, slides, 8mm, Super 8mm, or 16mm film onto videotape, you will need to Dummy-Plug your built-in microphone. To do this, go to the store and get a plug with a mini-male plug on one end and a female RCA on the other end (see illustration).

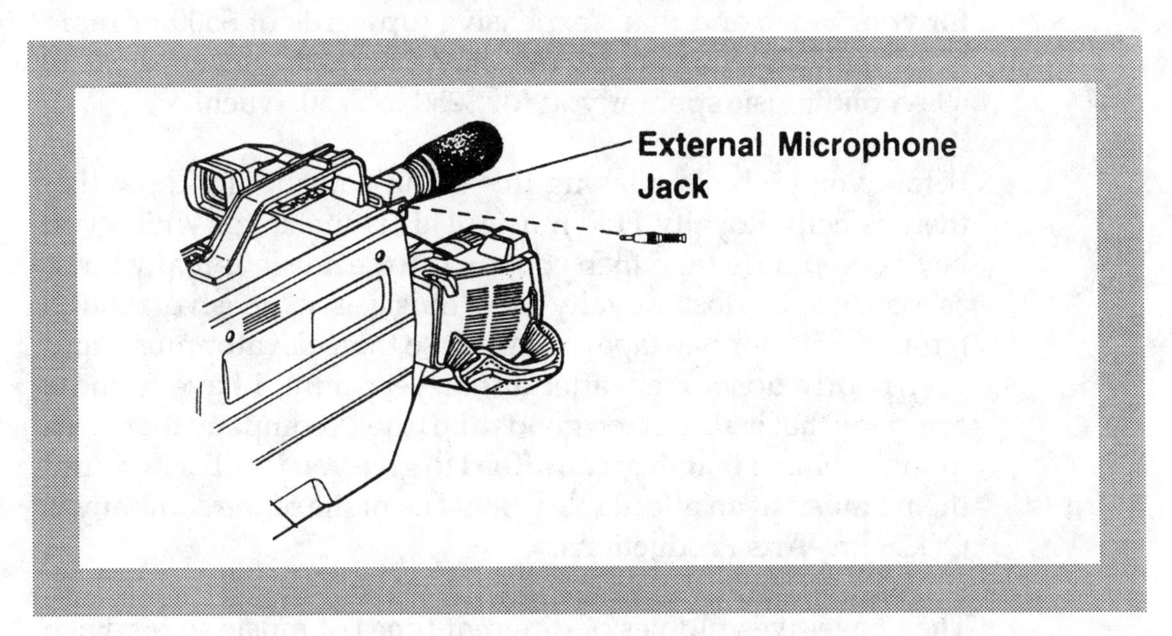

Connect this to your external microphone input, and *Voila!* No sound. If you don't do this you will get sound from the projector or people every time you turn on your Camcorder. Note: make sure you remove the plug to do everything else.

ROYALTY-FREE MUSIC

OK, you just finished that 30 or 60-second spot for a TV commercial; or the documentary that you worked on for six months for PBS; or you just finished a wedding and you want to add music. Where are you going to get the music? Music is copyrighted just like most books. Copyright infringement is big business for lawyers. You will have to buy rights to use music for your video and that's expensive (upwards of $500 or more per song). Of course you can have someone make a 30 to 60-second music spot for you for $250 to $750. Ouch!

Before you go broke playing this game you should know that there is help. Royalty-Free music. This is music for which you pay a one-time fee and then you can use the music as many times as you need. Most Royalty-Free music is expensive though (around $500 for one tape) or its worse than elevator music and very poorly done. Well, after a four-year hunt, I have found a company that is almost too good to be true. A company that deals in such volume that they can afford to give you Pro-Background theme music at an affordable price. The name of the company is QCCS Pro-Arts Productions.

They have five volumes of different types of music so far. Each volume of music includes:

- 10 to 12 themes (46-60 minutes of music).
- Professional Broadcast Quality.
- Available on Compact Disc or Chrome Cassette.
- 30 to 60 cuts on Volumes III, IV, and V.
- No royalty fees for the lifetime of the purchase.
- Two year warranty on CDs and Cassettes.

Volume I	Contemporary Variety
Volume II	Contemporary Variety
Volume III	Weddings and Soft Moods
Volume IV	Hot Tracks
Volume V	Contemporary Variety

This music is great for everything from TV commercials to film-to-video transfers; from weddings to graduations. All songs are different; all songs are great.

For a 24-hour demo (seven days a week) call (503) 345-0212.

The best part is the price: only $69.95 for Compact Disc or $59.95 for Cassettes and they are yours forever.

SOUND EFFECTS MIXER (BOING BOX™)

The "Boing Box" adds sound effects along with voice and music, to home videos! It's the first audio mixer with all the bells and whistles! The Sound Effects Mixer combines a three-channel audio mixer with a digital sound effects generator that can add any of 59 digitized natural sounds, plus a collection of electronic tunes and arcade sounds. Playing a sound is as simple as dialing a phone — simply press a two-digit number and the sound plays.

A digital "sequence player" allows you to program a sequence and play each sound as the action unfolds. To do this, simply press CLEAR and play several sounds. Then use the play button to play the same sounds again, in order. Up to 31 sounds can be stored in the sequence. The delete key makes it easy to remove an error.

The unit includes a series of automatic play modes. Three audio mini-plays use sound effects to tell a story, pre-programmed into the unit. You can play all the unit's sounds if you like, in order or randomly, with or without effects. You can also automatically play the sounds you've recorded in the sequence player. Special effects allow you to modify the built-in sounds. For example, play the car horn with the "LOWER" effect and it sounds like a bigger car. Play it "MUCH LOWER" and it sounds like a foghorn.

Stretch a sound like helicopter to make it last as long as you like. Add a pause to make stretched sounds come at various rates. For example, use this with footsteps or horse gallops to make a slow walk or a run.

The stutter effect gives sounds a r-r-r-rap effect. The fades repeat a sound, changing the volume so it sounds as if it's coming or going.

You can even play sounds backwards. Use the effects alone or together to make hundreds of different variations!

SPECIFICATIONS

The three-channel audio mixer adjusts sound from a microphone and two stereo sources. The stereo sources can include a cassette or CD player, VCR, receiver, etc. The digital sound effects are mixed into one of the stereo channels.

Output connections are stereo and a stereo headphone jack is included.

SPECIAL EFFECTS GENERATORS

In this section I will show you five systems out of several hundred on the market. These are the best and most useful for the full range of videographers. Read each section carefully and pick the right system for you, keeping in mind how much money you have to spend and what you want to be able to do, now and in the future.

VIDEO EQUALIZER

So, you want to be the new Ted Turner on the block or you just want to fix some dark or bad filming. The new Video Equalizer from Videonics is right up your alley. Here are some of the digital video things that this unit can do.

Digital Paintbrush and Colorizer: Adjust some of the colors in a scene without affecting others. Use the paintbrush controls to position an on-screen target on the color you want to change. Use the size control to determine how many colors you want to change.

Split Screen: Position the moveable split screen in an area of interest. The right side shows the enhanced and corrected image. The left side shows the unaltered image for comparison.

Enhancer: Use the sharpness control to sharpen the edges of objects for clearer video copies. A separate independent control reduces the snowy effects of video noise. The noise reduction and sharpness circuits are all digital for the best possible picture.

Dual Outputs: Two outputs for more flexibility. Allows you to make two recordings at once.

Video Processor: Brightness and contrast controls provide better adjustments than those on most TV sets. Use these controls also to fade to black. Boost the color to punch up dull video. Reduce it to subdue overly vivid scenes. Use the tint control to shift the colors in the entire scene, etc.

Three-Channel Audio Mixer: Add music or narration to your videotapes. These controls allow you to independently adjust the sound from a microphone, a music source, and the original videotape. Music and VCR sound channels are stereo.

Compatibility: The Video Equalizer is ideal for simple tape-to-tape copying or for use with video editors. This easy-to-use product is compatible with all videotape formats, including VHS, Super VHS, 8mm and Hi8. It connects to your VCR and Camcorders with either standard or S-Video (Y/C) connectors. All for the retail price of $549.

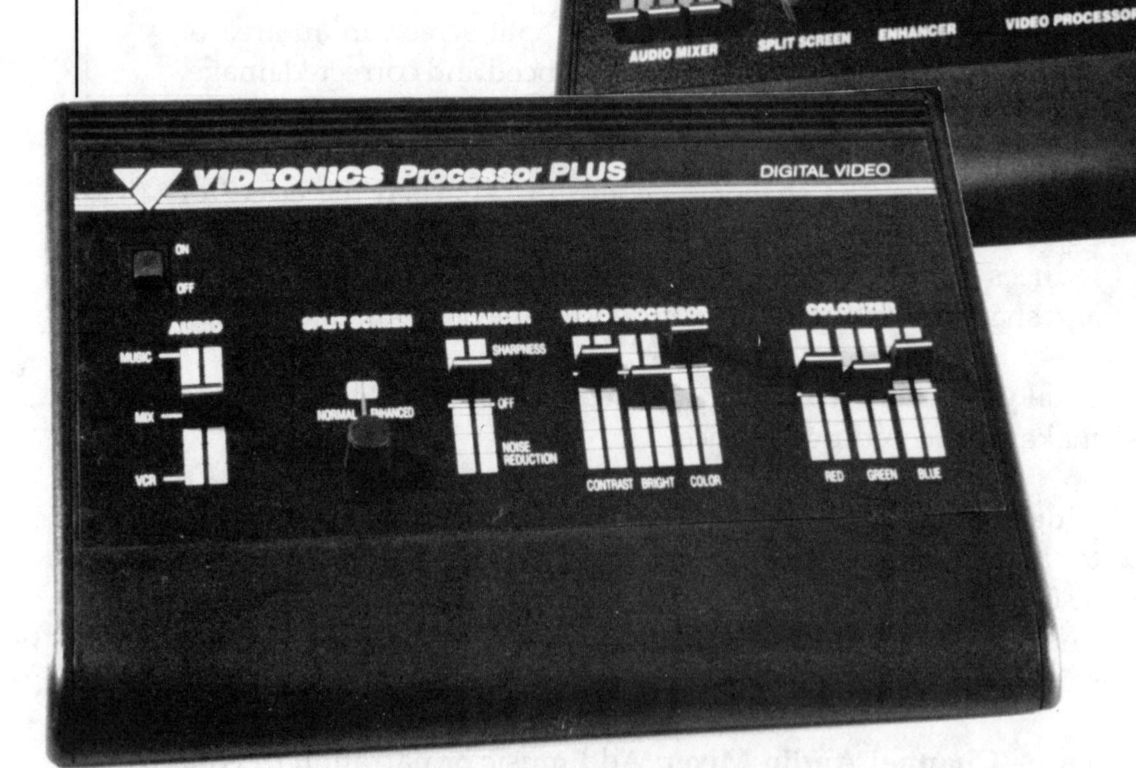

For further information contact:

Videonics
1370 Dell Ave.
Campbell, CA 95008

DirectED PLUS ™

If you are on a tight budget and can't afford $3000 or more for editing equipment, the DirectED PLUS is right up your alley for:

- Editing
- Adding Titles
- Special Effects
- Graphics
- Video Tape Library

Editing: DirectED PLUS automatically assembles your raw footage into a professional-looking video. It is possible to edit home footage by using the VCRs alone, but the process is very time consuming. DirectED PLUS employs computer controlled editing technology similar to professional editing consoles. It remembers all your scenes and edit points, and finds them for you automatically. Once you've settled on the exact order and length of the scenes, DirectED PLUS will assemble them into a finished production, removing all the unwanted footage automatically.

Adding Titles: Instead of buying a $250 small add-on character generator that does block type titles that you cannot superimpose after filming, the DirectED PLUS generates brilliant titles to give your videos that professional touch. Superimpose titles (without the need for a separate Genlock) over your footage or place them on a color background using DirectED's colorful digitally-generated graphics. Chose from 12 title styles and 64 colors.

Titles in 12 different styles can be superimposed over graphics or over the video itself.

Built-in graphics can be inserted anywhere in the final production.

Special Effects: You don't have to settle for haphazard transitions between scenes. Besides being able to cut from one scene to another, you'll be able to create Hollywood-style fades and wipes to connect scenes. Chose from 17 different types of fancy transitions including venetian blind fades, exploding wipe outs, and even some not found on the most expensive editors.

Graphics: Want to add some zest to your movies? DirectED PLUS has a library of built-in graphics you can insert into your video. You can even superimpose them right on your live-action footage.

Video Tape Library: DirectED PLUS also includes a computerized filing system for all your footage. You can even catalog hundreds of MTV-type music videos for easy access.

Remote control operation and on-screen instructions make DirectED PLUS easy to use and learn. All editing operations are done by remote control. Menus and instructions appear on your TV screen guiding you from one editing step to the next. There's even a Help! button that displays on-screen directions should you encounter a problem.

What's truly amazing about the DirectED PLUS is the price—under $700.

CANCEL =Done
S=Scene: Play time for Anne
=Search
SHIFT =FF/REW
=Mark scene start/end
SELECT =Save scene as marked
Start = 0:17:22.8
Now at 0:19:31.7
Length = 0:01:25.2
VIDEONICS

MID-PRICED SEG

For the under $2000 range in an SEG (Special Effects Generator) and Audio Mixer, I have picked Panasonic digital AV mixer WJ-AVE5 for several reasons.

1) Digital Synchronizer: The digital synchronizer allows you to mix video images from virtually any two sources such as VCRs, Camcorders or TV tuners without having to worry about whether the timing of the frames is the same.

2) Digital Special Effects: Things such as Still (Freeze), Mosaic, Digital Painting and Stroboscopic (a strobe-like effect).

3) Superimpose: For titling and graphics.

4) 98 different wipe patterns: You can do P-N-P (Picture in Picture) fully adjustable, control wipe direction and wipe boundaries, and even do multi-wipes.

5) Audio Mixing: Has three stereo inputs (Sources 1 and 2 are auxiliary) plus a microphone input. A clearly visible audio level meter ensures easy monitoring.

6) Video Title Keyboard: You can add the WJ-TTL5 CG (Character Generator) which includes time/stop-watch/date function as well as a memory function for frequently used titles.

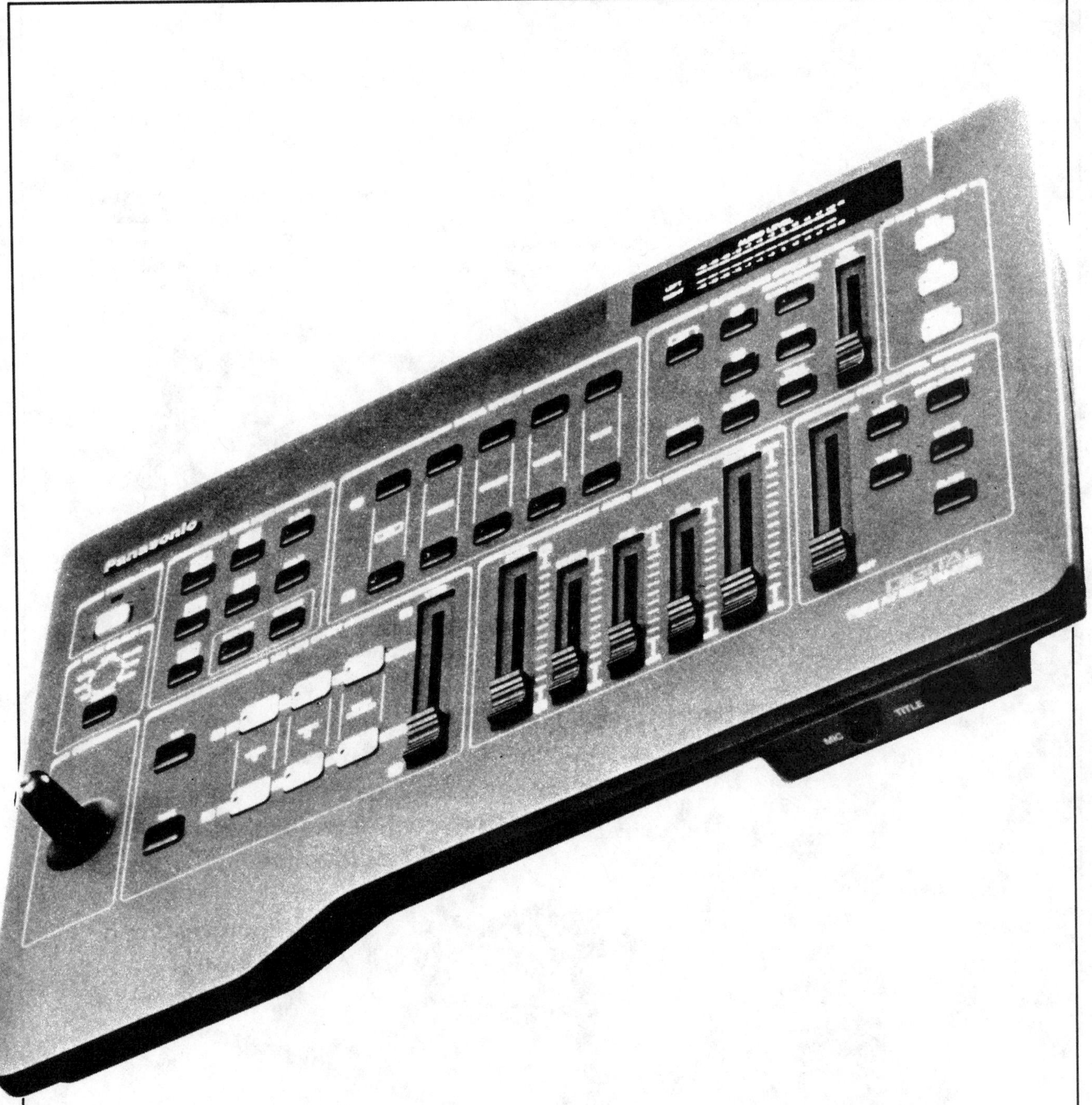

Retail Price: $1,995

For the nearest dealer in your area call (514) 633-8684(

VIDEO TOASTER

This remarkable new unit from NEWTEK Inc. is like a broadcast studio in a box. The video toaster is a unique computer-on-a-card that fits in the video slot of an Amiga 2000 or 2500 personal computer. The features are as follows:

Pop-Up Menu

The Video Toaster is controlled by the Amiga's icon operating system. Shown on this master menu are a wide variety of effects available to the user, such as freeze-frame, overlays, paint and 3-D graphics.

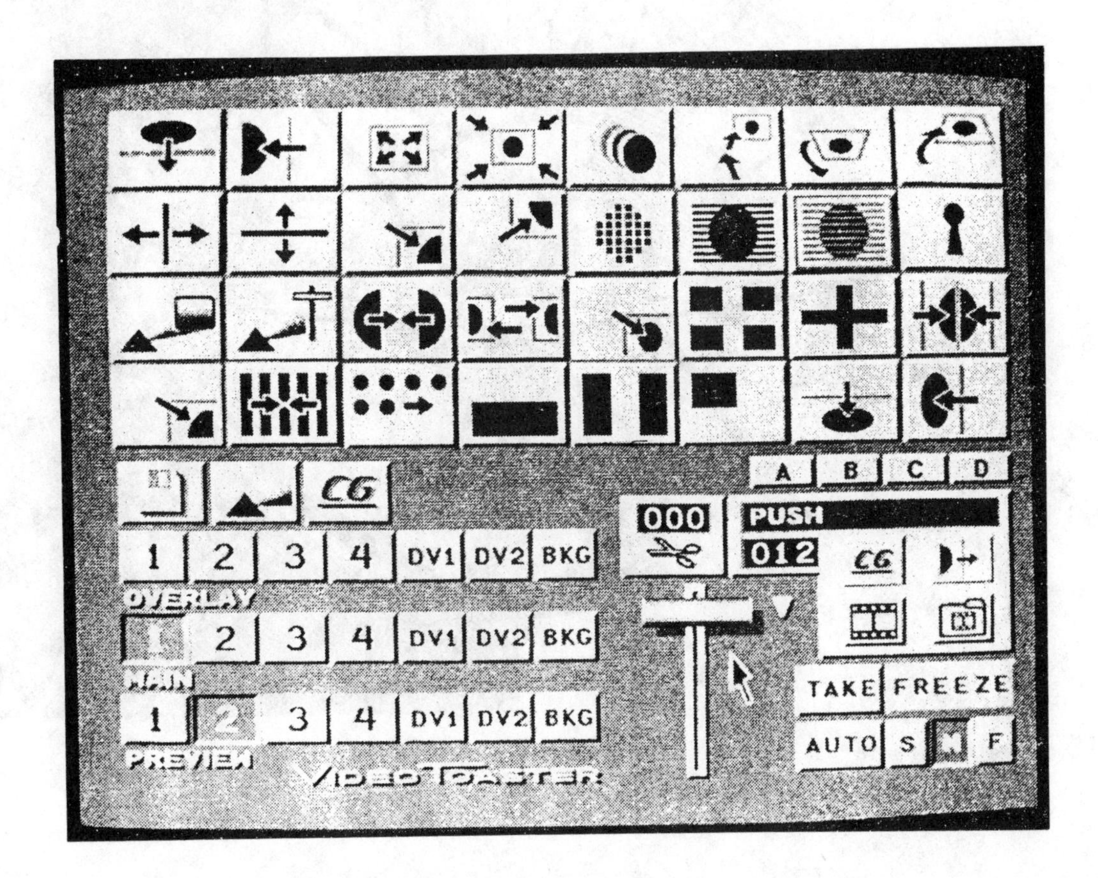

Four Input Production Switcher

The Video Toaster switcher replaces broadcast switchers costing tens-of-thousands of dollars. With it, you can perform cuts, fades, and wipes between any of seven sources including four video inputs, two frame buffers, and a color background generator. Use the built-in keyer to mix video images (i.e., a person superimposed in front of a weather map). Other advanced features include: two video outputs (program and preview), linear keyer, external GPI trigger, automatic or manual control. Unique features such as analog and snow trails make for eye-catching effects.

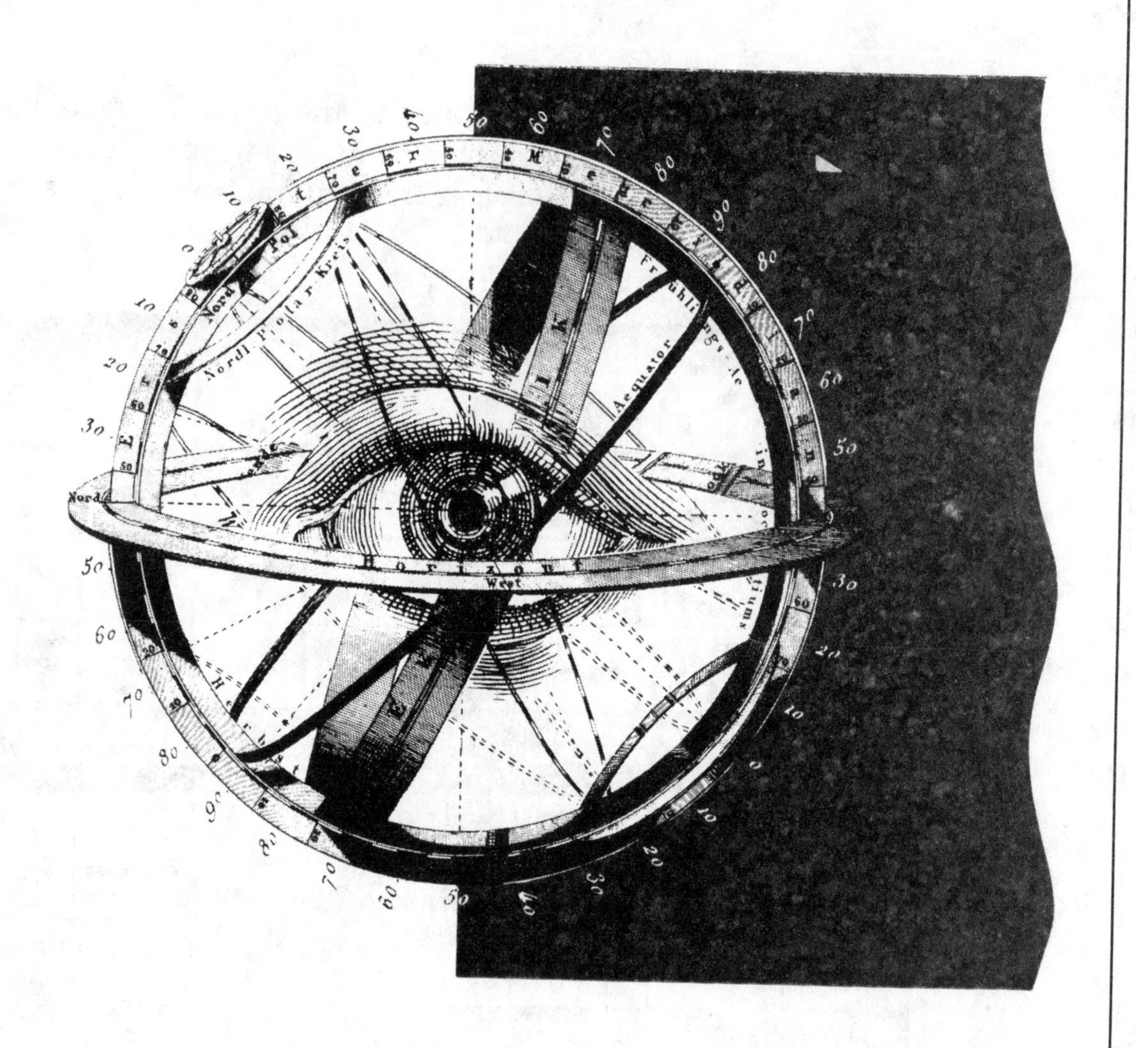

Digital Video Effects

Real time manipulation of live video. The Toaster can create hundreds of digital video effects such as Flips, Spins, Tumbles, Tiles, Curtains, Page Peels, Push-On and Off, Pulls, Expands, Slides, Mirrors, Splits, Stretch, Squeeze, Zooms (with variable borders), Blinds, Rolls, Slats, Mosaics, Trajectories, Strobes, and Digital Trails. There are also many original Toaster Digital Effects (TDE's) that are not possible with any other device including Whips, Zoom Trails, Luminance Dissolves, and the Transporter are just a few of the hundreds that you can perform.

LightWave 3-D Animation

Create animated videos in full broadcast resolution and 16.8 million colors. Lightwave 3-D offers many high-end capabilities previously found only in dedicated graphics workstations. Everything from flying logos and sports graphics to the most sophisticated effects seen on MTV are now within your reach. Some features are interactive wireframe editing with real-time feedback, real-time scene preview with "jog" shuttle control, fast photo-realistic rendering with adjustable anti-aliasing, 24-bit broadcast resolution output, fog effect with variable fog color and density, and multilayer image compositing with animated fade and dissolve.

LightWave simplifies 3D animation by using "key framing". LightWave 3D offers hundreds of advanced features including texture mapping, surface color mapping, diffuse and specular reflection mapping, environment mapping, transparency mapping, bump mapping, particle systems with motion blur, fog effects, multilayer image compositing, fractal noise and ray-traced shadows.

Toaster Character Generator

Add titles to your videos in 35ns resolution (the same as networks use). Features include 16.8 million colors, over 30 standard fonts, generation of semi-transparent shadows, variable outline and shadow, choice of drop or cast shadows, variable speed scroll and crawl, 24-bit smooth color gradations, 100 pages of on-line storage, and complete integration with the Toaster switcher including spinning, tumbling and zooming title screens. Use the included ChromaFonts such as brass, chrome, and rainbow to create dazzling graphic displays.

Toaster Paint

Gives you all the tools you need to create original artwork and amazing network quality videographics. Pictures can easily be colorized or recolored for photographic quality retouching. Includes powerful tools such as the ability to create original art or paint on grabbed video stills, anti-aliased texture mapping, warping and rotation. Complete drawing tools such as ellipse, rectangle, area fill, polygon and more. 11 drawing modes, including rub thru, blur, range, lighten and darken, text rendering, composite two or more frame store images together, cut and paste with any tool or any shape.

Dual Frame Buffers/Genlock

There are 16.8 million color frame buffers with full television resolution. The composite output meets the most stringent requirements for broadcast video. Because there are two frame buffers, one can be loading while the other is shown on screen for seamless live presentations. Toaster effects can be done between live video and either buffer, as well as between the buffers themselves. The Toaster allows overlaying Amiga mode graphics on incoming video or over either frame buffer.

Chroma FX Color Processor

This is a powerful color processing engine capable of producing color negatives, monochrome, solarization, posterization, color vignettes, custom lighting, tinting and photographic effects. Chroma FX will also allow you to subtly alter the brightness and contrast in different areas of the video image. You can design your own color effects with virtually limitless combinations or use any of the dozens built into Chroma FX. Standard effects include Nuke, Chrome, Snow Lights, Snow Cycle, Sunset Filter, Zebra Stripes, and many others. The stunning visual effects created with the Chroma FX are useful for applications from science fiction scenes to music videos to very subtle effects that might otherwise require difficult lighting.

Frame Grabber/Frame Store

The toaster can grab and save a full resolution television frame and provide a rock-solid freeze frame. These frames may then be loaded into Toasterpaint or Lightwave 3-D for further manipulation. Up to 1000 frames may be saved on each frame store device (depending on available storage space) stored frames can be loaded and displayed in the frame buffers in as short as 1/5th of a second from RAM or three seconds from hard drive. The Toaster also allows grabbing up to eight consecutive fields of live video and cycling the fields for animation.

Are you impressed yet? If not, how's the price of $1795 sound?

Right now the Video Toaster can only be used with the Amiga 2000 or 2500. You will also need at least five megabytes to kick it on, seven megabytes to run smoothly, but I would recommend nine megabytes; an 80 megabyte hard drive, and a TBC (Time Base Corrector) to mix two live video sources. I have put together a retail price list if you are starting from scratch.

Amiga 2000 or 2500 w/accelerator board	$3,500 to 5,000
Color monitor	350 to 400
Video Toaster	1,795
TBC (Time Base Corrector)	1,200 to 2,000
80 Megabyte Hard Drive	795
Extra Megabytes of Memory to bring total memory to nine megabytes	600
Total	$8,240 to 10,590

You can then add as many extra programs and goodies as you might want.

All in all you get more than you pay for.

For more information contact:

NEWTEK
215 S.E. Eight St.
Topeka, KS 66603
1-800-843-8934 or 913-354-1146

DESKTOP VIDEO

If you don't have the money or equipment to run the Video Toaster system there are alternatives if you own an Amiga. Below are some titling, paint, and animation programs and how to contact the companies that put them out. Most of these can also be used with the Video Toaster.

Titling

Broadcast Titler ($299.95), InnoVision Technology: First character generator to use super-high resolution with 320 colors per page.

InnoVision Technology
P.O. Box 743
Hayward, CA 94543

Pro Video CGI ($199.95), JDK Images: Professional full-featured high-resolution character generator.

JDK Images
15075 SW Koll Parkway, Suite GT
Beaverton, OR 97006

Paint

Deluxe Paint III ($129.95), Electronic Arts: Upgrade of very popular Deluxe Paint II, a versatile multi-resolution color paint program with some page-flipping capabilities.

Electronic Arts
1820 Gateway Drive
San Mateo, CA 94404

Photon Paint 2.0 ($99.95), Micro-Illusions: Versatile paint program with 3-D texture mapping functions.

Microillusions
17408 Chatsworth St.
Granada Hills, CA 91344

Animation

Videoscape 3D 2.0 ($199.95), Aegis: Quick solid-modeling program facilitates "phong" shading, transparency, and chrome effects all achievable in 4096 colors (HAM).

Aegis Development
2210 Wilshire Blvd., Suite 277
Santa Monica, CA 90403

Animate 3D ($149.95), Byte by Byte: Fully capable ray-tracing program with advanced animation features.

Byte by Byte
Arboretum Plaza II
9442 Capitol of Texas Hwy. N.
Suite 150
Austin TX 78759

PageFlipper Plus F/X ($159.95), Mindware International: Animation cell compiler, plus special effects.

Mindware International
110 Dunlop West
Box 22158
Barrie, Ontario, Canada L4M 5R3

The Director ($69.95), The Right Answer Group: Script-based program incorporates Basic-like commands to flip (full or partial) pages, play animation files, and add music and sound all at once.

The Right Answers Group
Box 3699
Torrance, CA 90510

Video Effects 3D ($199.95), InnoVision Technology: Create network-style digital video effects in true 3-D perspective.

InnoVision Technology
P.O. Box 743
Hayward, CA 94543

Some other companies to look into would be:

Computer System Associates
7564 Trade St.
San Diego, CA 92121

Digital Creations
2865 Sunrise Blvd., Suite 103
Rancho Cordova, CA 95742

Great Valley Products
P.O. Box 391
Malvern, PA 19355

MicroBotics
811 Alpha Drive, Suite 335
Richardson, TX 75081

Mimetics
P.O. Box 1560
Cupertino, CA 95015

NewTek
115 W. Crane St.
Topeka, KS 66603

Progressive Peripherals & Software
464 Kalamath St.
Denver, CO 80204

SPECIAL PRODUCTS

We have scoured the world to find products that would be of interest to the videographer. Anything to make our life easier, right? All of these products have been personally checked by me and they work! We also have information on how to contact any of the companies which make these products.

STEADICAM, JR.

Everyone is familiar with the Oscar winning invention the Steadicam. If not you should be. It's the remarkable invention of Garrett Brown and it's been used in movies such as *Rocky, Star Wars, The Shining, Indiana Jones and the Temple of Doom, Last Crusade, Aliens,* and hundreds of others. It costs around $40,000. I think that's a cheap price for what it does. It allows for camera operator filming movement and makes it more fluid, where it had been jerky and jumpy before. It is now used in almost every action movie in Hollywood.

You might ask what's in it for me? I don't have the 40 big ones to do a better wedding or follow a football game. Here's the story: Late 80's technology produced a new generation of 8mm, Hi-8, and VHS-C Camcorders weighing two to four pounds. While researching a device to stabilize this new video equipment Garrett Brown made a discovery that would eliminate the need for the Steadicam vest and support arm and the other features found on the Steadicam eliminating the need to carry around a 45 pound movie camera. Thus was born the Steadicam, Jr.

This versatile unit is of professional quality, has a built in power source for the monitor to run nine hours, a power supply for an orb light to run two hours. It runs off four standard "D" size batteries. It even comes with it's own carrying case and costs a lot less. Retail: Under $800.

My staff and I used this unit to see what it was all about. What started out to be a couple of hours of testing turned into two days of walking, riding, running, bicycling, roller coasting, and, yes, I even broke out my roller skates. Here are the results: Three of us did the testing. One of us got sick on the roller coaster (the Steadicam did great); the bicycle built for two will be out of the shop soon (the Steadicam did wonderful); the car trips were superb; and the trip to the park was fantastic.

This is where I would suggest practicing with your Steadicam, Jr. It does take a lot of practice to be really good. Don't expect to hook it up in ten minutes and off you go. You have to learn to flow with the unit. You actually have to build a relationship with the Steadicam, Jr. When you do you will want to use it on everything from weddings to graduations to races.

VIDEO TITLEMAKER

The Video TitleMaker uses Digital Video Technology to deliver unprecedented quality and performance. It is the first consumer/industrial titler capable of broadcast-quality resolution, with 720 pixels per line and 480 lines. It surpasses S-VHS/Hi8 resolution and outperforms professional units at several times the price!

Titles, backgrounds, outlines, and borders can each use any of more than a million colors. You're not limited to ordinary solid colors — "patterns" such as "granite" or "shimmering rainbow" are available. Some patterns are animated!

The four (at this writing) smooth, high-quality fonts each come in five sizes, including huge letters, a third of a screen high! Each line of text can use a different size, font, and color.

Many enhancements are possible, including drop shadows, several grades of bold letters, outlines, scrolling, and much, much more. Every word can use a different enhancement. Titles can be superimposed over moving video and can scroll up, down, right, or left. You really must see these titles to appreciate the quality!

Borders can be added in many styles, such as boxes, lines above or below text, and vertical or horizontal lines anywhere on the screen. The borders on each page can use a different color and pattern.

The TitleMaker is not limited to a fixed number of "pages" of text. Depending on how many characters of text are on each page, it can hold hundreds of pages.

The TitleMaker has a complete computer-style (QWERTY-layout) keyboard. Accented characters (such as é, ü, ç) for over

16 languages are easily accessed using the special "ACCENT" key.

There's no complicated setup procedure. Take it out of the box, connect it to a television/monitor or VCR, and type! It's easy to change colors, title styles, etc. Press one of the color-coded buttons (such as "Background Pattern") and choose from the on-screen palette.

Advanced yet easy to use editing functions make it simple to copy and move text, etc. Two-speed positioning controls make it easy to locate a spot on the screen, for typing or changing. The "Undo" key lets you fix a mistake instantly.

The Video TitleMaker includes conventional and S-video (Y/C) connectors.

VIDEONICS™
THE VIDEO EDITING COMPANY
1370 Dell Ave., Campbell, CA 95008-6604 • USA • 408-866-8300

VIDEO TITLEMAKER

ALL WEATHER FILMING

Video filming has always been a no-no in inclement weather, because contact with rain, snow, dust and sand will destroy a Camcorder, UNTIL NOW!

The EWA Marine Video Cape is a hood that's made of rugged, yet flexible PVC that fits over any Camcorder, keeping it dry and safe from rain (it can't be sunny all of the time), spray (beach scenes in Hawaii), or snow (skiing).

I personally film a lot of yacht races. I used to have my Camcorders thoroughly cleaned after each filming session because of salt water exposure, until I got the Video Cape. While a thorough cleaning on a Camcorder is between $100 and $170, the retail price of the Video Cape is between $150 and $175. Sounds like a deal to me.

FILMING THE FISHES!

If you have ever wanted to film underwater (where the action is), now's your chance. Imagine capturing colorful reef scenes and seascapes without the fear of your Camcorder going down the drain (a small attempt at humor). Your trip to Hawaii or the beaches in LA would be far more spectacular with some under the water scenes.

EWA has come to your rescue (so to speak) with their new U-VCMG housing that will accommodate all of the recently introduced Super VHS Camcorders produced by Panasonic, Olympus, Chinon, Nikon, Quasar, Magnavox, and General Electric. The new EWA housing features a huge 140mm optical glass port for distortion-free images. Also included for divers is a weight pack which can hold up to 9 pounds of lead shot or dive weight to neutralize buoyancy. The weight pack has three pockets and sits under the Camcorder in the housing.

This unit is totally waterproof. I was a little hesitant, but they show you how to test the unit first. I tried the unit at the swimming pool and it was great! Then I tried it at Lake Mead (in the housing of course) and with about 30 onlookers (probably betting on me or the Camcorder drowning), off I went into the great waters. I emerged after being engulfed in a feeding frenzy and was immediately whisked away to the nearest pub with a TV. While washing down free pretzels with FREE BEER we all watched what I had filmed. To make a long story short, the bets were paid (in favor of me and the Camcorder), and the filming was superb, mainly because they were shot where the fish were (in the water). Next week the Colorado river and I'm sure the EWA Marine Housing will hold up better than I will.

The price for this gem is between $400 and $500 depending on 8mm or VHS formats. A price WELL WORTH IT, for just one trip to the great deep (or even Lake Mead).

Pioneer Marketing & Research, Inc.
216 Haddon Ave, Suite 522
Westmont, NJ 08108

Waterproof your camcorder!

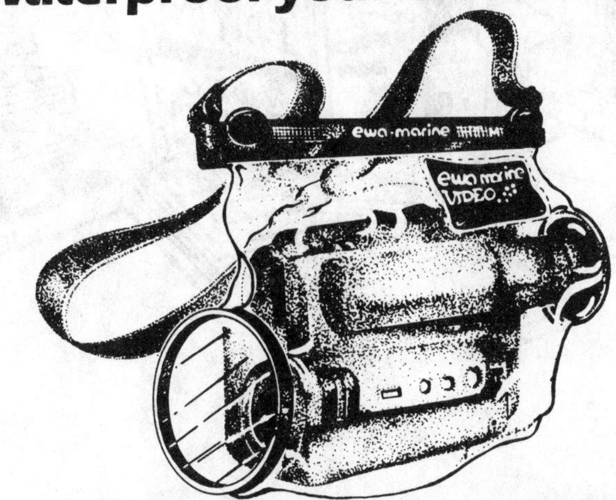

ewa-marine housing for the Sony TR-5!

- 100% waterproof protection
- 90mm optical glass port
- Safe to 30 ft. underwater
- Capture the action with the spacesuit for your camcorder!

GLOSSARY OF VIDEO TERMS

(The Most Complete Group of Video Terms Anywhere)

VIDEO GLOSSARY

AC (Alternating Current): An electrical signal whose voltage fluctuates between positive and negative values. Standard US household current is 120 volts, 60 hz.

AFC (Automatic Frequency Control): A feature which compensates for slight tuning misadjustment.

AFT: Automatic Fine Tuning.

AGC (Automatic Gain Control): Minimizes picture differences with changes in strength of the incoming signal.

Amplifier: AC-powered device that restores signal loss occurring during transmission.

Audio Dubbing: With the audio dubbing feature you can change the audio on an original video tape without changing the video portion. This is great at a party when you start and stop the camera often. This gives you the ability to go back and add some music to the whole tape.

Auto Focus: Found now in almost every Camcorder. It allows the Camcorder to focus the lens automatically.

Beta: A format that came out in 1975 by Sony. It uses half-inch videotape in a cassette.

BTSC (Broadcast Television System Committee): The US version for multi-channel television sound (MTS). Provided for two-channel stereo and an optional mono SAP (Separate Audio Program) channel that is used for purposes such as bilingual broadcasting. Developed by Zenith and DBX.

Cable Ready: Without the use of a cable converter box. Able to receive unscrambled channels (Basic Service), including mid-band and super-band channels.

Camcorder: This is a video camera and video recorder (VCR) in one unit.

Capstan: A flangeless pulley used to control speed and motion of magnetic tape through a recorder or playback unit.

Cassette: A type of tape cartridge containing two reels.

CCD (Charged Coupled Device): It is an image sensor that replaces the old video tube. It is more durable and vibration resistant and does not need any warm-up time.

CDV (Compact Disc Video): A type of compact disc that can store up to five minutes of video with digital audio, in addition to 20 more minutes of digital audio.

CG (Character Generator): This lets you add titles either during filming or at a later date (depending on what type of Character Generator you have).

Chrominance: A signal that carries the color information to produce a color picture on a TV or Monitor/Receiver.

Coax: An abbreviation for "Coaxial". The standard single-ground, single-conductor cable used for video connections. Also referred to as 75 ohm, RG-59U cable.

Color Processor: An electronic video accessory used to control the color response of the picture.

Comb Filter: A circuit used in some Monitor/Receivers and in most VCRs and Camcorders to improve the separation of the luminance and chrominance signals, which results in a sharper picture.

Compatibility: The ability to use one piece of video or audio system equipment with another.

Component Video: A videophile (I hate that word) system that has separate high-quality goodies, like Hi-Fi VCR, Monitor/Receiver, good stereo, laser player, and shielded speakers.

Control Head: The VCR head responsible for recording and reproducing a control signal that keeps the video head synchronized with the tracks or the video tape.

Convergence: A specification that rates how well the three scanning electron beams used to produce a color picture are aligned. Beams that are misaligned degrade the quality of the picture.

Converter: AC-powered device that converts low-band channels to mid-band or high-band reception.

Coupler: A video accessory that combines two or more video signals into one.

CRT: Cathode Ray Tube is another name for a picture tube.

db **(Decibel):** a measure of sound, volume or strength.

dbx: The noise-reduction system used by BTSC (MTS/SAP) stereo TV decoders. It takes the compressed audio signal that is transmitted and then expands the signal to its original dynamic range.

DC (Direct Current): An electrical current that does not alternate.

Degausser: A device to demagnetize a color picture tube for color purity.

Depth of Field: The amount of distance between the closest and farthest points in focus as seen by a video camera. The higher the F-Stop number, the greater the depth of field.

Detailer: An electronic video accessory that allows you to increase the apparent sharpness of a picture.

Dew Indicator: This indicator will automatically operate if there is excessive moisture in the unit and will shut the unit down for a period of time, usually 30-60 minutes.

Digital Sound: The method by which 8mm stereo sound and compact discs are recorded. Analog audio is converted to a string of numbers that represent pitch and loudness at any given moment. The numbers are recorded on video tape or other media and are converted back to an analog sound signal for reproduction.

Diopter: An adjustment on many electronic viewfinders which compensates for the user's differences in vision.

Distribution Amplifier: An active form of signal splitter that allows a single video source to be connected to two or more video components.

DOC (Dropout Compensator): A circuit used in most VCRs to hide dropouts. It operates by substituting a portion of the previous line for the missing segment.

Dolby: An audio noise-reduction system used to reduce noise on stereo linear-track audio.

Dolby Surround Sound: An audio system that takes rear-channel information from broadcast signals, videotapes, and laser disc with Dolby Stereo encoded soundtracks. You need at least three speakers.

Dropout: A loss of picture signal during tape playback which appears as a black or white streak in the screen.

Dubbing: The copying of a tape or the adding of new information to the tape.

8mm: This refers to the tape or film width. There are now two types of formats with 8mm. They should have been called 8mm video, 8mmV or something like that. To date, about 20% of the people in the USA think that 8mm video has to be developed, because of the confusion between 8mm movie film and 8mm video tape. (No joke.)

Edit: To rearrange a video recording by playing back and re-recording segments in a different order, adding new video and/or audio and deleting unwanted material.

Ed Beta (Extended Definition Beta): A better version of the Beta format that has better horizontal resolution. Something similar to S-VHS.

EIS (Electronic Image Stabilizer): A new feature for Camcorders to compensate for camera movement. A servo mechanism, while using digitals, "floats" the lens or picture to compensate for movement so you don't get shaky pictures.

Electronic Switcher: A video switcher that uses active components to affect signal routing.

Enhancer: A circuit which can improve video quality by boosting the high-frequency content of the video signal. Enhancers can be sold as an accessory or in some cases are built into the VCR.

EP (Extended Play): The slowest record/play speed for VHS VCR. It also has the poorest picture quality. Also known as SLP (Super Long Play).

Erase Tab: A small plastic flap on the rear edge of a video cassette that can be removed to prevent accidental erasure of the cassette.

Event: Used to describe the capacity of a VCR's timer. One event consists of turning on the VCR at a specified time, recording from a designated channel, and then turning off after a preset duration.

EVF (Electronic View Finder): This stands for electronic view finder. Simply put, it is the little TV in the eyepiece of your Camcorder.

Faroudja Circuit: Named after Yves Faroudja, this system is a signal booster that improves picture clarity and sharpness.

Field: One half of a completed TV picture consisting of only the odd-or-even numbered lines. To minimize flicker, TV pictures are sent at twice the normal rate by first sending the even-numbered lines and then filling in the missing odd-numbered lines. A single TV field contains 262.5 lines of information, half the normal vertical resolution of 525 lines (NTSC).

Flying Erase Head: Simply put, this gives you clean edits and cuts between scenes. It's a shame if you don't have it on your Camcorder.

Footlambert: A measurement of light that is emitted or reflected from a surface. Used in rating the brightness of projection Monitor/Receivers; the better the rating the better the brightness of the picture. A good rating is 300 or more footlamberts.

Format: A set of standards which determine all aspects of a video recording system.

Frame Advance: A special effect that stops on-screen actions on most VCRs and video disc players and allows you to advance one frame at a time. Used to check out frame-by-frame action. There are 30 frames per second in video.

Freeze Frame: A special effect that stops on-screen action.

Gain Up: You use this button in extremely low light conditions. The picture may become grainier.

HDTV (High-Definition Television): A future TV system that has higher resolution, and a more horizontal picture than current US Television.

Heads: Small electromagnets used to record and reproduce magnetic patterns on video tape.

Helical Scan: A term used to describe the way the tape is wrapped around the video head drum and the diagonal tracks created by this wrap.

Hi8: A higher resolution version of the 8mm video format.

Hi-FI: In video, refers to high-quality stereo AFM (Audio Frequency Modulation) sound with quality close to that of a digital recording.

High Speed Shutter: You can record fast-paced movement with the high speed shutter switch on. Then, while in the playback mode or slow mode, a VHS (VCR) will show you the fine points of any motion at 1/1000th, 1/500th or 1/250th of a second with no blurred screen image. I think this feature is more hype than anything. Also, it really jumps your LUX dramatically, so only use this outside with plenty of available light.

HQ High Quality: It provides much better pictures than a non-HQ unit. Just about everything in VHS is HQ.

Horizontal Resolution: Rating the detail of a Monitor/Receiver or TV picture. It is measured in lines. The more lines the better. A standard VHS VCR produces approximately 160-240 lines of horizontal luminance resolution. S-VHS and laser disc players are around 330.

Hue: Color set control governing color values in TV picture; also called tint.

HZ (Hertz): A unit of frequency equal to one cycle per second.

Index/Address Search System: With this system the unit automatically records an index and address signal onto the tape (invisible to us). You can also manually record an index mark later on a unit with this system. Then, you can locate specific points on the video tape in the fast forward or rewind mode.

IPS: Tape speed in inches per second.

Laser Optical: A system of video recording on grooveless discs, employing a laser-optical-tracking pickup.

Lead-In: A wire or cable from antenna to TV set.

Linear Audio: A conventional sound recording system that uses stationary heads and a thin track that runs along the length of the tape.

LM (Lumen): A unit of light intensity.

LP (Long Play): The middle record/play speed for VHS VCRs (four hour mode on T-120 video tape), and the slower speed for 8mm models.

Luminance: The part of a video signal that causes a televisions circuitry to vary light intensity from white to black with many shades of gray in between. This signal alone creates the picture on a B&W TV set; a color picture is produced when a luminance signal is combined with a chrominance signal.

LUX : This is a measure of brightness. One LUX equals one candlepower.

Macro: This feature lets you view small objects incredibly close.

Mhz (Megahertz): A unit of frequency equal to one million hertz.

Moiré Line: Irregular, wavy, vertical line found at the beginning of a video recording made with a Camcorder or VCR without a flying erase head.

Monitor: A separate video unit that houses a picture tube and it's electronics. It must be connected to a TV tuner, VCR, video disc player or computer to display a picture.

Monitor/Receiver: A video monitor with built in TV tuner, and at least one speaker. It has RCA-type audio and video inputs and may have outputs, avoiding the need for signal degrading found in RF (antenna) signals. Many Monitor/Receivers now have five video inputs as well.

MOS (Metal Oxide Semiconductor): Another type of solid-state, light-sensitive pickup.

MTS (Multi-channel Television Sound): A term covering any system for putting more than one channel or sound on a TV signal.

Noise: Any unwanted electrical signal that interferes with the sound or image being communicated.

Non-interlace scanning: A video display system in which all the lines of a video frame are scanned in order. Also can be done using digital processing to generate non-interlaced images from standard interlaced signals.

NTSC (National Television Standards Committee): The name for the television broadcasting system in the US and the rest of North America, as well as in Japan and some other countries. Carries 525 scan lines per second.

Optical Viewfinder: A viewing device that uses an auxiliary lens rather than a small TV monitor. No playback of previously-recorded video is possible with an optical viewfinder.

PAL (Phase Alternation by Line): The name for the television broadcasting system used in most Western European countries and some other parts of the world. A PAL system carries 50 frames of 625 interlaced scan lines per second.

PCM (Pulse Code Modulation): A fancy name for digital sound recording. VCRs with PCM are characterized by exceptionally low noise and a wide dynamic range; a step beyond Hi-Fi.

Phase: Describes the relative synchronization of two video signals of the same frequency.

Pick-Up Tube: A light sensitive tube that converts an optical image into an electronic signal which can then be converted onto video tape.

Projection TV: A large-screen television that uses a special optical apparatus to project images onto a screen or wall. Screen sizes range from 36-60 inches, projecting onto a wall 100 inches or higher.

Protection Circuits: Sensors that shut down the VCR or Camcorder to prevent any damage to the unit or video tape if certain criteria are not met.

Resolution: The amount of detail in a TV picture.

RF: Radio frequency.

RF Modulator: An electronic circuit that converts video signals into a standard TV broadcast frequency.

RGB (Red, Green, Blue) Input: An input found only on High-end video Monitor/Receivers, and monitors for connection of a personal computer or professional video equipment with RGB outputs.

Record Review: While in record/pause mode you can use the EVF (electronic view finder) and the record review buttons to check the last few seconds of video tape just recorded. This lets you make sure that your shot came out the way you wanted.

SAP (Separate Audio Program): An optional mono channel in the MTS system which allows a station to broadcast in addition to its regular stereo signal. The common application is for bilingual transmissions.

Scan: Also referred to as search. This enables the user of a VCR or laser disc unit to move quickly forward or backward through the video tape or video disc with visible image but no sound.

SECAM (Système Electronic Pour Couleur Avec Mèmoire): The French name for the broadcasting system used in parts of Europe and a few other parts of the world.

SEG (Special Effects Generator): This lets you add a multitude of special effects like color borders, strobe effects, screen dividing, etc. depending on the unit.

Shuttle Search: A feature that allows a picture to be seen while the tape is running at high speed forward and reverse.

Simulcast: Also known as FM simulcast. This VCR feature enables you to record audio from your FM tuner or Receiver onto a video tape.

Slow Motion: A special effects feature found on most VCRs that lets you view images in slow motion without sound. Most can even adjust the speed of the slow motion.

SLP (Super Long Play): Same as EP.

Solid State: Commonly used to indicate use of semiconductor devices in place of tubes.

S/N (Signal-to-Noise Ratio): A relative measurement of the amount of unwanted background noise in a video or audio signal.

SP (Standard Play): The fastest record/play speed of a VHS VCR and 8mm VCRs. This speed will give you the best recording and should be the only speed you use in your Camcorder.

Splitter: A device used to split an incoming signal and to route it to at least two components.

Stabilizer: A circuit that compensates for missing sync pulses in video recording that have been protected against copying.

S-VHS (Super VHS): A VHS format that has greater horizontal luminance resolution. Approaching or slightly exceeding that available from standard broadcasts.

S-Video (Separated Video): Also called L/C (Luminance/ Chrominance). A type of video connection (often mistakenly called an S-VHS connection) that carries the luminance (brightness) and the chrominance (color) information of a video signal separately.

Switcher: A component that helps the interconnection of several video sources in one system.

Time Shifting: Recording a TV program for later viewing on your VCR.

Tracking Control: Even though the tape speed of VCRs is set at the factory, there may be a slight difference from one VCR to another. The tracking control is used to adjust your VCR to compensate for any difference in speed and match that of a previously recorded video tape from another VCR.

Transport: The VCR mechanism responsible for the physical handling of the video tape.

TV Tuner: A video component that contains circuitry needed to tune television or cable channels. It is connected to a video monitor to make a Monitor/Receiver.

UHF (Ultra-High Frequency): Television signals located on channels 14-88 on US TV tuners.

VCR: (Video Cassette Recorder): The video tape is in a cassette format.

Vernier Tuning: Continuous fine tuning.

VHD (Video High Density): System of video recording on grooveless discs employing electronically-guided capacitance pickup.

VHF (Very High Frequency): Television signals located on channels 2-13 on US TV tuners.

VHS: Uses 1/2 inch video tape contained in cassette form. The VHS format was first introduced by JVC in 1976.

VHS-C: A type of VHS format using 1/2 inch video tape in a mini-cassette. For use mostly in VHS-C Camcorders. A full size VHS adapter must be used to be played on most VHS VCRs.

Videographer: A person who uses portable or studio video equipment, such as a Camcorder, to take moving pictures of objects or events, especially as an occupation.

Videography: The art or process of producing images of objects by the use of portable or studio video equipment such as a Camcorder.

Video Disc: A medium that stores information (picture and sound) on an optical video disc. Retrieved from the disc by a laser pickup on a laser disc player. Laser disc sizes include 5, 8 and 12 inches in diameter.

Video Dubbing: The video dubbing feature added with the advanced rotary flying erase head technology allows you to very cleanly replace a segment of video tape with a new segment without any lines of color bar distortion moving down the picture (moiré line). This feature and the audio dubbing feature should be a couple of the top things you consider and look for before you buy your Camcorder.

Video Heads: Used to record and read video signals on a video tape. Basic VCRs use two heads; more expensive models have three, four, five or more heads. The extra heads are used primarily for Hi-Fi sound and to improve the quality of special effects such as slow motion, pause/still, and single frame advance.

Video Input: An RCA input jack found on Monitors or Monitor/Receivers. Used to connect a video source (VCR, SEG or Computer) giving the best picture quality.

Video Processor: AKA Proc Amp, also known as a single processor. Usually used to prevent signal loss when dubbing tapes from one VCR or Camcorder to a second VCR.

Video S/N (Signal to Noise Ratio): A specification that rates the amount of video noise (snow or a generally grainy texture) in a picture. Ratings of 38 to 42 db are typical. Those above 45 db are excellent.

Volt: The unit of electromotive force equal to a force that when steadily applied to a conductor whose resistance is one ohm will produce a current of one ampere.

VTR (Video Tape Recorder): The video tape is in a reel format.

White Balance: A control on Camcorders that adjusts for varying light sources to produce accurate color. Automatic on most models.

WOW: A slow variation in the pitch of a reproduced sound. A component with excessive WOW sounds like a warped record.

Y/C Inputs: The luminance (brightness) and the chroma (color) jacks in the back of a VCR or TV. Same as S-VHS (Super-VHS) input.

Zoom: This feature makes objects that are far away appear closer.

I would like to point out two words that we are particularly fond of. The words are Videographer and Videography. These two words, as of January, 1991 will be in Webster's College Edition. After 16 years in this business and hearing people calling themselves "Video Photographers" or "We do Video Photography", or videographers called "Videophiles", I wrote Webster's to finally get the "right words" into a dictionary. So, now it's official! I just can't stand someone calling himself a "Video Photographer", unless of course he only uses a "still video camera".

Smiley-Cam™

SENNHEISER
ON OFF
MKE 300

CAMCORDERS THAT PLAY AS HARD AS YOU DO
If you're looking for *the* name in Camcorders that you can depend on to work as hard and play as hard as you do — you're looking for Hitachi. Hitachi Camcorders are built for those of you who demand nothing less than exceptional performance everytime. Whether the Super VHS or this Hi-band 8 mm format with Hi-Fi stereo sound you'll record pictures with startling clarity and colour. Every one of the many advanced features will tell you — This is *the* Camcorder to strive for.
HITACHI
Exceptional Performance
HITACHI
Hi-Fi STEREO SOUND
Hi8
FULL AUTO
DATE
REVIEW
SHUTTER
WHITE BAL
IRIS
AUTO
x8
NORM

CRISPER, CLEARER SOUND, AND A BRILLIANT PICTURE - ONLY ALLSOP'S PATENTED VCR CLEANING SYSTEMS CAN *THOROUGHLY* CLEAN THE HEADS, CAPSTAN AND PINCH ROLLER FOR THE ULTIMATE IN VCR PERFORMANCE.

ALLSOP'S VCR CLEANERS USE A PATENTED, NON-ABRASIVE CLEANING RIBBON THAT IS ALTERNATELY WET AND DRY. THE WET PORTIONS DISSOLVE HARMFUL CONTAMINANTS WHILE THE DRY PORTIONS REMOVE THEM FROM THE VCR. AND, *ONLY* ALLSOP CLEANERS FEATURE A SPECIAL CLEANING CARTRIDGE THAT SCRUBS THE CAPSTAN AND PINCH ROLLER TO HELP PREVENT TAPE DAMAGE.

CLEANERS ARE AVAILABLE IN VHS/S-VHS, 8MM AND VHS-C FORMATS.

ALL ALLSOP PRODUCTS COME WITH A TOLL-FREE 800 CUSTOMER ASSISTANCE LINE AND ARE AVAILABLE WITH A LIFETIME GUARANTEE.

- PATENTED CAPSTAN AND PINCH ROLLER CLEANER TO HELP PREVENT TAPE DAMAGE.
- ALTERNATING WET AND DRY, NON-ABRASIVE CLEANING RIBBON.
- THOROUGHLY CLEANS AUDIO AND VIDEO HEADS FOR OPTIMUM PERFORMANCE.

NOTES SECTION

Direct Re-Order Form

Name: ______________________________

Address: ______________________________

City: ____________________

Province: ____________________ Postal Code: ____________

Telephone Number: (   ) ____________________

I would like to order the following books:

	# of Books	Price Each	Total
Everything You Always Wanted to Know About Video	____	$16.95	____
Everything You Always Wanted to Know About Camcorders	____	$15.95	____
Everything You Always Wanted to Know About Home Video Editing	____	$19.95	____

Please Add 3.50 (per order) Shipping & Handling

Grand Total ____

Send payment to:

SGH PUBLICATIONS Inc.
2320 St. Louis
St. Lazare, Québec
J0P1V0

Call for Dealer Prices (514) 426-8130